SMALL BOAT
ENGINES

SMALL BOAT
ENGINES

A Comprehensive Handbook
Covering the Care and Maintenance
of Inboard and Outboard Motors

by CONRAD MILLER

Illustrated by Allen Beechel

HART PUBLISHING COMPANY, INC.

New York City

Library of Congress Card Number 61-17772

PRINTED IN THE UNITED STATES OF AMERICA

SMALL BOAT
ENGINES

TABLE OF CONTENTS

SMALL BOAT
ENGINES

Chapter One

HOW MARINE ENGINES WORK

THERE IS a world of outward difference between a fisherman's one cylinder, cast iron "banger" and a sleek, smooth-purring, eight-cylinder, high-speed marine engine, yet they are the same basic breed of cat. Their essential features and principles of operation are identical. The big eight-cylinder job is more complicated than the single-cylinder putt-putt only in duplication of parts and addition of elaborate accessories, but the underlying principles of operation remain the same. The very bulk of a large marine engine may frighten you when you think of maintaining it; but on the other hand a light weight auxiliary looks deceptively simple. The fact remains, however, that if you understand one marine engine, you understand them all. They are not like women, they are quite rational and their design is based upon scientific principles.

The best way to find out how a marine engine works is to look right inside a simple one and see what makes the flywheel go 'round.

It is the process of burning or exploding a combustible mixture within the cylinder which actually makes the engine tick. The term "explosion" is a bit misleading in view of the fact that the activity inside the cylinder is not a wild explosion in the military sense, but is a smooth, progressive burning of fuel and air. This is true whether the engine burns gasoline or is a diesel.

Consider, for a moment, an engine which is running properly. Just before combustion the cylinder is filled with a mixture of gasoline and air, compressed into the top part of the cylinder. At a precise instant a spark jumps the points of the spark plug and starts the mixture burning. The mixture, however, does not explode all at once with a shattering crash, but burns progressively over a finite period of time, depending upon how fast the engine is spinning. If the gasoline is of poor quality or the engine is overheated or the ignition is too early, the mixture may detonate violently, causing "knock" which is so widely discussed on the billboards.

There are two kinds of gasoline marine engines in current production. Most inboard engines are four-cycle, and most outboard's are two-cycle. First, let's take a look at the basic functioning of the four-cycle engine (Fig. 1).

The heart of the engine is its cylinders and pistons, and in the head of each cylinder there are two valves. The inlet valve opens and closes to admit the combustible mixture into the cylinder at the right time during the cycle, and the exhaust valve opens after combustion to let the hot, burned gases escape. The valves are not opened and closed by the force of the gases or by action of the piston, but are worked by special valve gears built into the engine for just that purpose. A pipe or manifold leads from the inlet valve to the carburetor so that all air drawn through the inlet valve is mixed with gasoline first. Another manifold is connected to the exhaust passage to conduct away burned, spent gases to the exhaust pipe.

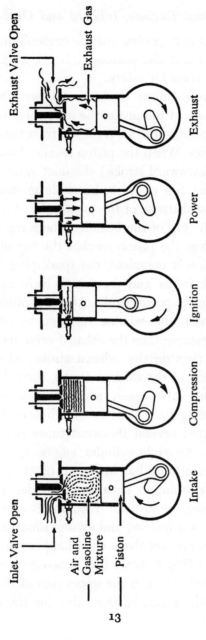

Fig. 1. The basic functions of the four-cycle gasoline engine.

Inlet Valve Open

Air and Gasoline Mixture

Piston

Exhaust Valve Open

Exhaust Gas

Intake   Compression   Ignition   Power   Exhaust

13

The exhaust from a gasoline marine engine is not only hot and smelly but it is also poisonous, hence a tight exhaust system is important for safety.

The four-cycle engine works as follows: On the first downward stroke of the piston the inlet valve is open and a mixture of gasoline and air is sucked from the carburetor into the cylinder. When the piston reaches bottom center (end of the downward stroke) the inlet valve closes and traps a cylinder full of fresh, burnable mixture. On the following upward stroke of the piston, the charge is compressed into the top of the cylinder where the spark plug is located. When the piston reaches the top of its stroke and compression is complete, the spark plug ignites the mixture which burns and creates pressure to force the piston down on the power stroke. After the piston is forced to bottom center, the exhaust valve opens and lets the burned gases escape; then the exhaust valve remains open as the piston rises on the exhaust stroke. At top center after completion of the exhaust stroke, the exhaust valve closes, the inlet valve opens, and the cycle is repeated.

In a fast turning marine engine the whole cycle of events may be repeated several thousand times per minute in each cylinder. An eight-cylinder engine spinning 3,000 revolutions per minute has to digest 12,000 separate explosions every minute! Is it any wonder that spark and valve timing are critical? Wouldn't it sound crazy if someone proposed igniting and extinguishing 12,000 bonfires every minute? Yet that's what happens in an engine.

Reference to Fig. 2 shows that a two-cycle engine has no cam-actuated valves in the upper part of the cylinder. There is usually a simple flap valve for the carburetor inlet and the piston acts as a valve for the inlet port and exhaust.

The two-cycle engine works like this: The power stroke and exhaust function are combined into one downward movement of the piston, and the intake and compression are combined in one upward movement. The carburetor does not have any connection to the cylinder but feeds into the crankcase which is airtight and which has a passage leading to the cylinder. On the upstroke of the piston

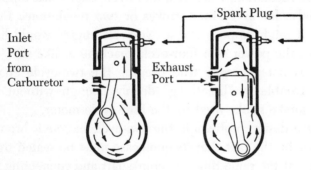

Fig. 2. *Inlet and exhaust porting of the two-cycle gasoline engine.*

the combustible mixture is compressed above the piston in the combustion chamber. When the piston reaches the top of its stroke, the mixture is fully compressed and is ignited by the spark plug. Burning of the charge generates pressure which pushes the piston down on the power stroke until the exhaust port is uncovered and the spent gases rush out the stack. The piston continues down still farther on its stroke and finally uncovers the inlet port through which fresh mixture pours into the cylinder and the cycle starts over again.

Because the crankcase is sealed, and because there is a check valve on the carburetor throat, the downward stroke of the piston compresses the mixture in the crankcase; hence when the inlet port is uncovered by the piston, the crankcase pressure pushes fresh mixture into the cylinder and helps push exhaust gas out of the exhaust port.

You can see that a two-cycle engine has a power impulse for every two strokes of the piston or for every single crank revolution, whereas a four-cycle engine has a power impulse for every four strokes or two revolutions. From this it might appear that a two-cycle engine would have twice the power of a four-cycle machine of like size; but this is not generally true because the two-cycle engine has trouble in "breathing" deeply enough without the full intake stroke used by the four-cycle motor.

One design problem in the two-cycle engine is brought about by the fact that its crankcase must be sealed tight, while at the same time the crankshaft and connecting rod bearings within it must be lubricated. Under ordinary circumstances lubrication of the bearings would be very difficult indeed, as they are working in a steady stream of gasoline and air which would wash away the lubricating oil. Instead of lubricating the bearings in the usual way they are lubricated by adding oil to the gasoline so that as the fuel passes through the crank-case it will lubricate the bearings. For this reason it is important to follow the manufacturer's recommendations in adding lube oil to outboard motor gasoline. Failure to add the correct amount of oil to one tankful of fuel would probably wreck the motor.

The reason that outboard motors and other two-cycle marine motors give off a blue haze of smoke is, of course, because lube oil is added to the fuel. The gasoline burns cleanly, but the oil burns with a characteristic odor and light blue smoke.

Modern diesel engines are similar to gasoline engines in many ways, and they are made in both two- and four-cycle types. However, while most two-cycle gasoline en-

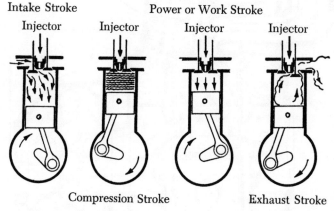

Fig. 3. *The basic functions of the four-cycle diesel engine.*

gines are small ones (outboards for example) two-cycle diesel engines are built in all sizes, including the famous General Motors line of diesels used in many yachts.

The sequence of operations in a four-cycle diesel (Fig. 3) is very much the same as in a four-cycle gas engine; however, on the intake stroke clean air is sucked into the cylinder of a diesel rather than fuel/air mixture. The air is compressed to very high pressure and the extreme compression heats the air to a torrid temperature; then, when the piston is near top center, fuel oil is sprayed into the cylinder through an injector. The air is so intensely hot that all the oil bursts into flame and the subsequent com-

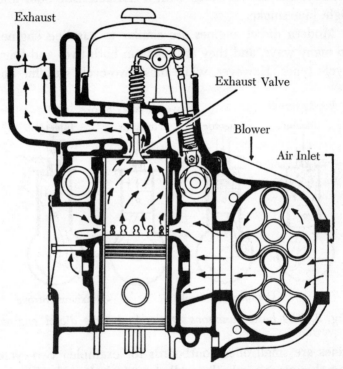

Exhaust

Exhaust Valve

Blower

Air Inlet

Fig. 4. *Exhaust porting of the two-cycle diesel engine.*

bustion creates still higher pressures which drive the piston down on the power stroke.

Arrangement of valves, manifold, et cetera, is substantially similar to that of the gasoline engine and the injector takes the place of the spark plug. Naturally, there is no electrical ignition system.

The two-cycle diesel engine (Fig. 4) incorporates important differences from its two-cycle gasoline counterpart: Crankcase compression is not used, the engine has poppet valves, lube oil is not mixed in the fuel, crankcase lubrication is conventional, and a separate engine-driven blower, or super-charger, is used to get combustion air into the cylinder.

The sequence starts with the piston at bottom position, the inlet ports are open and the valve in the head is also open; the blower pumps air through the cylinder to scavenge dead gas from the prior combustion and to furnish fresh air for the next. The top valve closes and the piston rises to cut off the stream of incoming air; the piston continues to rise on the compression stroke. Near the top of compression when the air is heated to terrific temperature, fuel injection takes place and the piston is forced down on the power stroke. When the piston is down about two thirds of the way, the exhaust valve opens in the head and allows the hot exhaust gas to rush out, then the piston continues down and uncovers the inlet port so that fresh air can be pumped in to scavenge the cylinder and start the cycle anew.

All conventional gasoline marine engines have a carburetor for metering and mixing a given ratio of gasoline and air so that the mixture will burn in the cylinders (Fig. 5). A carburetor is not a device to "gasify" or vaporize the gasoline, but is simply an instrument to measure out and mix a correct amount of fuel with a given amount of air. The actual work of gasifying or vaporizing the gasoline is done in the inlet manifold by contact with the hot valve surface, and in the cylinder itself. Most good marine carburetors differ from automobile carburetors in that they are constructed of heavy castings, are equipped with anti-drip features and a backfire trap. You will notice that most modern updraft marine carburetors have the

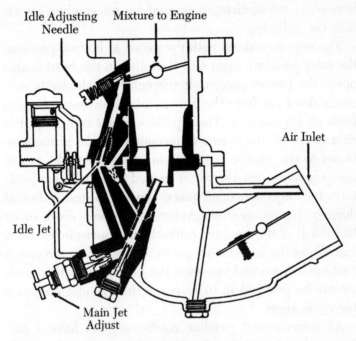

Idle Adjusting Needle

Mixture to Engine

Air Inlet

Idle Jet

Main Jet Adjust

Fig. 5. *A typical marine engine carburetor.*

air intake turned slightly upward. This prevents backfires from aiming at the bilge (a danger spot for fumes) and it prevents gasoline from dripping out of the intake into the bilge after the engines are shut down.

All gasoline marine engines are fitted with one or more spark plugs in each cylinder. The spark plug's job is to ignite the combustible mixture at an exact instant. But while the spark plug's job is very simple, there are complex design considerations in the manufacture of a plug for a given service. The proper plug for a particular engine is a careful design balance between running too hot or fouling up. It is desirable that the plug run hot enough to rid itself of carbon deposits and soot, but it must not get excessively hot lest it pre-ignite the mixture within the cylinder. Another factor entering into spark plug performance is gap clearance, the space between electrodes within the cylinder. If the gap is too large the engine may be hard to start and may run unevenly at advanced throttle; if the gap is too small the engine may perform poorly at all speeds and the plug may foul up prematurely.

In a diesel engine the spark plug is replaced by the fuel oil injector which is usually a removable assembly fastened into the engine head. The injector is a precision-made device which sprays the fuel into the combustion chamber as a mist, and the timing of the injection is as critical to a diesel as spark timing is to a gas engine. The precise timing of injection is controlled by one or more cam-actuated pumps which are driven by accurate timing gears.

Timing of the spark in a gasoline engine is carried out by the distributor or a magneto. Marine engine ignition systems are essentially the same as those on auto engines with the exception that some are better protected against moisture and some have radio interference shielding. Almost all modern marine ignition systems have automatic spark advance which varies spark timing to suit engine

speed; hence the old-fashioned spark control lever is missing from newer boats. Modern marine magnetos are
fitted with an impulse coupling, a device to give the spark
an extra shot in the arm when the engine is cranking
slowly.

A few marine engines are air cooled, but the great majority of both gasoline and diesel engines are water cooled.
The water cooling system of a modern marine engine is
somewhat similar to that of an automobile or tractor engine, but there are important differences. Marine engines
have a heavy water jacket around the exhaust manifold,
and most of them have provision for cooling the lubricating oil. In addition, some engines have added piping so
that cooling water may be circulated through jackets in
the clutch and reduction gear assemblies.

Cooling of the exhaust manifold and oil in a marine
engine is necessary because the engine operates in a con-
fined space without the blast of outside air enjoyed by
an automobile engine, and the marine engine works much
harder (Fig. 6). Without adequate cooling a marine engine would literally run red hot and would be a menace
in any boat. Since only about thirty per cent of combustion heat is turned into useful work, the balance of the
heat must be eliminated somehow. Some of the heat is
blown out of the exhaust, some is radiated directly from
the engine, but the remainder must be carried away by
the cooling system.

Every marine engine has a lubrication system, even
though on some small engines it may be no more than
a pan of oil and a pipe or two. On some large engines it
may consist of several pumps, many finely drilled pas-

sages, coolers, trays, pipes, by-passes, valves, gauges and whatnot, but on all marine engines the function is the same: to reduce engine friction to limit wear, and to lower bearing temperatures. Most modern engines have a full-forced lubrication system wherein oil is sucked from the sump by a gear pump and sent under pressure to the bearings of the crankshaft, camshaft and wrist pins. On many engines the oil is circulated through a filter and also through an oil cooler. The oil cooler is a heat exchanger ar-

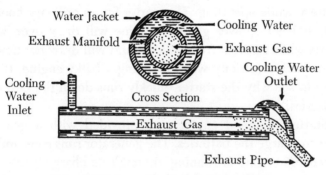

Fig. 6. *Water-cooled exhaust manifold.*

ranged so that the hot lubricant runs through tubes or passages that are surrounded by cool water, the water being pumped through by the cooling water pump. An automobile engine gets along without an oil cooler because it operates in a turbulent stream of air created by the car's motion and the fan. A marine engine, on the other hand, is buried in stagnant air which affords little or no natural cooling and, what's more, the marine engine works much harder and throws more heat load on the lubricating system.

In ye olde days it was customary to start a marine engine by hand cranking, but modern Americans do not look kindly upon such calisthenics and so virtually all inboard engines and many outboard motors are fitted with electric starters. A starter is simply a very powerful, low-voltage, electric motor with a gear drive which couples and uncouples automatically from the flywheel. Most starter motors for gasoline or diesel engines operate on 6, 12, or 24 volts, and, inasmuch as they are small but very powerful machines, they draw terrific current from the battery while operating. The starter for an ordinary house cat, 100 horsepower gasoline engine will draw over 300 watts while running free, no load, and will draw ten times that much electricity when cranking a balky engine. It is easy to see why the starter quickly runs down the best of batteries.

Starter-equipped engines are provided with a generator to charge the batteries. The generator runs constantly when the engine is running although its charging rate is varied to suit battery needs. The generator charges the batteries at a much slower rate than the starter depletes them. For example, if a starter draws 300 amperes for half a minute to start a stubborn engine, the generator will take an hour to recharge the battery, provided the charge rate is 10 amperes and the overall charging efficiency is fifty percent. Naturally, if there are other demands upon the output of the generator (as for lights and ignition) the charging will be slowed.

Chapter Two

TURNING FUEL AND AIR INTO POWER

THE AVERAGE motorboat owner is not overly concerned with the deeper ramifications of marine engine design or combustion theory; however, he is forced to be interested in keeping his engine in repair and occasionally doing some adjusting or trouble-shooting. If he understands his engine and has a pretty good picture in his mind of what makes it tick, his chances of doing the intelligent thing at the right time are good. So keeping the trouble-shooter and tune-up man in mind, we will take a closer look inside the cylinders of a smoothly purring marine engine.

After the intake stroke has filled the cylinder with the combustible mixture, the piston rises, compressing the mixture into the combustion chamber where it will be burned. Spark jumps the plug points before the piston has reached top center because a required amount of advance is needed. Ignition advance is necessary because the mixture does not burn instantly, but requires a finite interval. When the spark flashes it starts a very tiny nucleus of flame within the combustion chamber, and several milliseconds of time are consumed getting this small bit of flame to spread and ignite the balance of the mixture. The faster an engine speeds, the more must the spark advance, for as the speed increases, the amount of time allowed for flame travel decreases, making it necessary to snap the spark earlier. In other words: if an engine requires spark advance of 10 degrees at 1,000 r.p.m., it will require about 20 degrees at 2,000 r.p.m. (Fig. 7). In modern marine engines the spark advance is matched to the speed

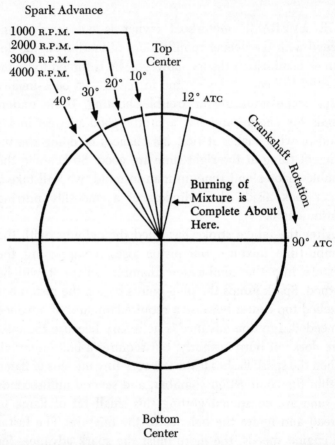

Fig. 7. *This graph shows how spark timing is advanced in accordance with engine speed.*

by means of centrifugal weights in the distributor body, but it is still necessary for the mechanic to manually set the initial timing.

Another factor which changes the necessary ignition advance is the alteration of mixture richness: A weak mixture burns slower than a rich one, so that when the mixture is weakened it is necessary to advance the spark to compensate for the sluggish flame. An engine burning a lean mixture will sputter, pop and cough through the carburetor unless the spark is advanced sufficiently.

After the mixture has been ignited and burned with consequent raising of cylinder pressure, the piston descends on the power stroke. If spark timing is correct and combustion is proper, maximum cylinder pressure could occur approximately twelve degrees after top center, then decrease until the exhaust valve opens and drops the pressure to atmospheric. The worst deviation from this ideal cycle is when knock or detonation takes place. Modern, high performance, high compression V-8 marine engines are very prone to detonate, and when they knock, not only is their performance ruined but their innards as well. Here is why:

Detonation and pre-ignition are not the same thing; they are separate and distinct phenomena, and an engine may suffer from one without the other, although in some cases both may torture the engine at the same time.

Pre-ignition is igniting of the charge within the cylinder before the spark has jumped, and is caused by a local hot spot such as an overheated spark plug, a hot valve, or an incandescent piece of carbon. Detonation, on the other hand, takes place after the spark.

Let us look inside an engine which is knocking (Fig. 8):

In an engine suffering from ping, the intake and compression are normal and the igniting of the mixture by the spark plug is also quite normal. The compressed mixture

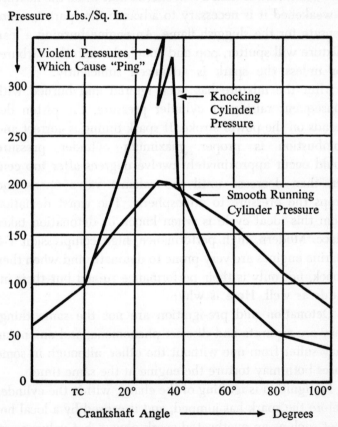

Fig. 8. *Pressure curves inside the cylinder of a gasoline engine showing the difference between smooth normal pressure and violent hammering which accompanies detonation.*

starts to burn, the flame starts to spread in a proper, progressive manner, but before burning has gone far, the complete charge of mixture suddenly explodes wildly, like dynamite. The reason for the sudden detonation is the fact that the first part of the mixture burned along a "front" compresses the unburned portion of the charge ahead of it, thus raising the temperature of the remaining mixture to a self-ignition point with the result that it all exploded at once with a shattering crash. The release of energy is so sudden that the gases strike the cylinder walls, head and piston top with a hammerlike blow, resulting in the familiar ping or knock often discussed on the billboards. When an engine is detonating heavily its power falls off because, instead of the gases within the cylinder exerting a steady pressure on the piston, they merely strike it a glancing, vicious blow resulting in less useful thrust.

For years, detonation has been the limiting factor on the power and thermal efficiency of gasoline marine engines. The greatest cause of detonation is high compression, and since raising the compression ratio also raises thermal efficiency and power, it follows that detonation is a great limiter of marine engine brawn. However, in the last few years marine engine people have made a break-through with the help of the gasoline manufacturers, and have brought out very high compression, valve-in-head, V-8 engines which have enormous power in a small package. These engines will not ping if correctly tuned and operated on high octane gasoline tailored specifically for them. But, by the same token, these hot, V-8, high-compression engines cannot be operated on "regular" gasoline if detona-

tion is to be avoided. The use of "regular" gasoline neces-
sitates retarding the spark (which is hard on the valves;
and operating at reduced throttle in order to avoid pinging. So let us face it, if you are going to retard the spark
and half close the throttle, why get the souped-up engine
in the first place?

Returning again to the inside of the cylinder, it is observed that turbulence or velocity of the mixture within
the combustion chamber has the favorable effect of reducing detonation. When the mixture is highly turbulent
the flame from the spark plug spreads faster and starts
more flame fronts, like a forest fire in a tornado, consequently there is less chance for a "front" to form and to
compress the remaining charge to self-ignition point. An
engine designer cannot utilize unlimited turbulence, however, because the rate of pressure rise would become so
steep that the engine would run roughly and be subject
to unnecessary stresses. When an engine runs fast, there
is more turbulence than at slow speed, and boat opera-
tors will observe that an engine will knock less for a given
throttle setting after the engine has accelerated and come
up to steady speed. There is also less knock when a correct propeller is used rather than an oversize wheel which
loads the engine to less than rated speed.

Diesel engines have extremely high compression ratio
and burn low grade fuel. Why don't they knock?

A properly tuned diesel will not knock because the fuel
starts to burn at almost the exact microsecond that it is
sprayed into the cylinder, and burning continues progressively as the fuel is injected. Therefore, there is never an
appreciable volume of unburned mixture within the cylin-

der which can detonate. It is like a kitchen oven with the gas burner turned on: if the gas flame keeps burning there can be no dangerous mixture in the oven, hence no explosion. But if the gas is turned on for a while and the flame ignited, the result will be most noisy.

There are cases where diesel knock can occur due to the use of poor quality fuel which has slow ignition qualities. In this instance, the fuel will have ignition lag and will not start to burn instantly as it is injected, hence a charge of unburned mixture will conglomerate in the chamber. Then when burning starts belatedly, detonation will occur.

Note that most diesels have a mild knocking sound even when running properly. Many high-speed diesels sound like a gasoline engine which is detonating lightly, but this is only due to the high pressures and is accepted as the nature of the beast.

Pre-ignition cannot plague a diesel because during compression stroke there is no explosive charge in the cylinder; there is nothing but plain air.

But let us return now to the cylinder of a normally operating gasoline marine engine (Fig. 9): after combustion is finished and the resulting pressure has driven the piston down on the power stroke, exhausting of the hot gases takes place. The exhaust valve opens considerably before the piston hits bottom center on the power stroke. The exhaust valve is opened early in order to reduce pressure in the cylinder to only a few pounds, at most, by the time the piston is ready to start up again on the exhaust stroke. The reason for this is easy to fathom: if there were considerable pressure in the cylinder when the exhaust stroke started, the pressure would work against the piston and

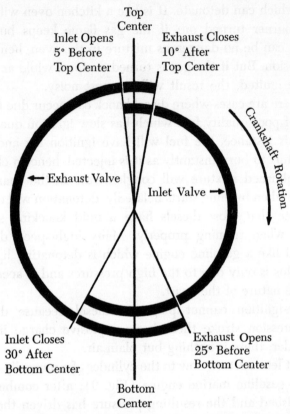

Fig. 9. *Valve timing diagram of a low speed marine engine.*

try to slow the engine; it would be a reverse boot-strap operation with the engine trying to stop itself.

Modern high speed V-8 marine engines are timed to have very early opening exhaust valves because the faster an engine spins the earlier must the exhaust valve open to allow the spent gases time to escape and avoid back pressure (Fig. 10). On some hot racing engines operating at ultra speed, the exhaust valve starts to open eighty degrees before bottom center!

Four-cycle diesel engines have valve timing patterns very similar to four-cycle gasoline engines, and of course the two-cycle diesel engine with exhaust valves in the head is timed to have the exhaust opened very early to assure

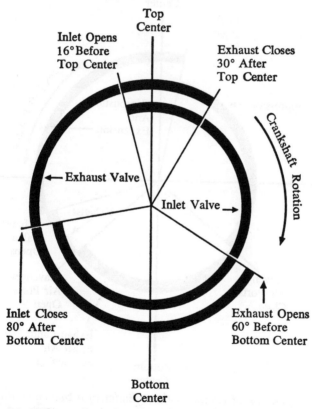

Fig. 10. *Valve timing diagram of a modern, high-speed, V-8 marine engine. Notice that the exhaust valve opens long before the power stroke is completed.*

that cylinder pressure is substantially reduced before the piston uncovers the air inlet port. (Fig. 11). On this type diesel, such as The General Motors series 71, if the exhaust valves were not opened early enough to relieve pressure, there would be considerable blowback into the scaven-

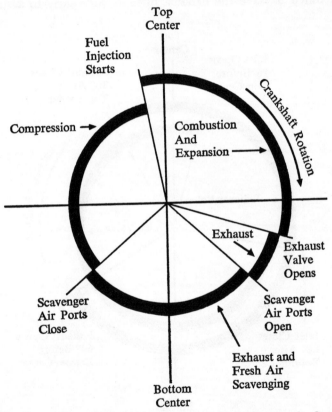

Fig. 11. *Timing of events in the cylinder of a two-cycle diesel marine engine. Notice the short interval allowed for exhaust and scavenging.*

ger blower and the engine would rebreathe exhaust products rather than fresh air on the intake cycle.

The exhaust stroke in a four-cycle gasoline or diesel engine might better be called the scavenger stroke, because most of the dead gases rush out through the exhaust valve at the bitter end of the power stoke and early start of exhaust stroke, leaving only small residuals behind. On the exhaust stroke the piston travels up to top center and pushes out these stray gases thus leaving the cylinder quite clean; not completely clean, however, because there are still dead gases in the combustion chamber where the piston cannot reach. It is apparent, then, that a high-compression engine will retain less exhaust gas in the cylinder at the completion of the exhaust stroke than will a low compression machine; consequently there will be less inert gas in the combustion chamber to dilute the fresh incoming charge of mixture. This is one of the minor reasons why a high-compression engine is more powerful than a low-compression one, both machines being otherwise equal. It is not only the simple dilution of fresh mixture which reduces power, but also the fact that the residual exhaust gases in the cylinder are very hot and they expand the incoming charge, thus reducing its weight and lowering the breathing ability of the engine.

In view of the above it should be apparent to the boat owner why it is important to install an engine with exhaust pipe sizes recommended by the manufacturer, and why sharp bends or obstructions in the exhaust pipe should be avoided. Small pipe, undersize muffler or any restriction in the exhaust system results in back pressure and consequent bottling up of exhaust gas in the cylinder; this results in poor engine breathing, loss of power, and overheating the exhaust valves.

Returning again to the cylinder, it may be remembered that the exhaust valve opened considerably before the piston started on the scavenger stroke; similarly it does not close until after the piston has reached top center and started down again on the intake. The reason for this closing lag is that exhaust gas, like all other earthy matter, has weight and inertia. Once the exhaust gas starts whistling out of the exhaust valve at terrific speed, it will keep on racing due to pure momentum. Thus, even after the piston has stopped rising, the exhaust valve stays open a short time longer to allow the last dregs a means of escape due to sheer velocity. Exhaust valve lag of 18 degrees after top center is fairly typical for gasoline marine engines.

The inlet valve opens just a trifle before top center, stays open during the downward intake stroke of the piston and remains open considerably after the piston has passed bottom center and has started compression. The weight and momentum of the inrushing mixture keeps filling the cylinder even after the piston has reversed direction and started compression.

An interesting and typical example of high-speed gasoline marine engine valve timing is that of the Graymarine Fireball V-8:

Intake valve opens ..... 16° before top center
Intake valve closes ...... 80° after bottom center
Exhaust valve opens .... 60° before bottom center
Exhaust valve closes .... 30° after top center

Let us leave the inside of the cylinders now and look at the frothy activities inside the carburetor and inlet manifold:

As air whistles through the carburetor it is mixed with

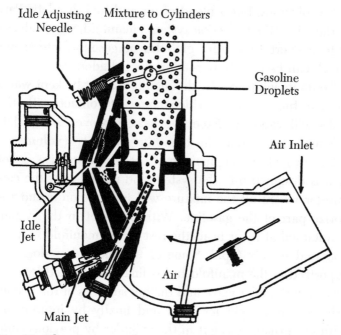

Fig. 12. *The marine carburetor is a device to meter gasoline and mix fuel and air together; but it does not vaporize or "gasify" the mixture.*

liquid gasoline in the ratio of about fourteen to one by weight, or roughly ten thousand to one by volume (Fig. 12). Note that the carburetor does not magically convert raw gasoline into gas or vapor, it merely sprays small drops and tiny blobs of liquid fuel into the rushing stream of air. After air has raced through the carburetor and been mixed with gasoline in the proper ratio, it passes to the riser and the manifold in mixture form. When the mixture first arrives in the manifold, it is not a homogeneous batter of gases, but a blend of air and fuel droplets. Part of the job of the induction system (manifold, riser, valves) is to convert these tiny globules of gasoline into vapor which can be readily burned in the cylinder.

To do its job properly, the manifold must be kept warm so that fuel particles which come in contact with the walls will vaporize. Excessive heat, however, has a detrimental effect upon the breathing capacity (volumetric efficiency) of the engine. To effect a compromise, a hot spot is designed into the system and placed near the carburetor where all the mixture will impinge on it and vaporize part of the gasoline. With one spot in the system maintained at fever heat, the rest of the manifold may be operated merely tepid. Some of the fuel never does get vaporized in the manifold but is finally vaporized by contact with the inlet valve and the hot surfaces of the piston, exhaust valve, cylinder head and finally by intermixing with hot exhaust gas left in the cylinder by previous combustion.

The two-cycle outboard engine has no orthodox inlet manifold, and vaporization of the gasoline must be accomplished in the crankcase by contact with hot engine parts and in the cylinder by contact with the hot piston and by intermixing with hot exhaust residuals.

The diesel engine deals very simply with the problem of

fuel vaporization by eliminating the need altogether. Because the fuel is sprayed into the cylinder directly and is burned as it enters, no intake manifold is required excepting for a very simple one to handle pure, cool air.

Chapter Three

HOW MARINE ENGINES ARE COOLED

AS YOUR BOAT speeds along through the foaming water and the engine purrs steadily, a lot of gasoline or diesel oil is being burned in the cylinders of the faithful power plant. The combustion of all this fuel generates plenty of heat. Unfortunately only a quarter to a third of the heat is converted into useful work, the balance is sheer waste and must be eliminated before it damages the engine. The function of any cooling system is to carry away waste heat before it can become a destructive nuisance.

The large majority of marine engines, both gasoline and diesel, are water cooled, but there are some small engines such as the little Briggs & Stratton or Wisconsin, and some small outboard motors which are air cooled. These modest size machines have individual cast cylinders covered with fins around the cylinder head and barrel. These fins provide the cylinder with enough surface area to transfer all its waste heat to the cool stream of air rushing past. However, no matter how well finned the cylinder may be, it will operate excessively hot unless fresh air is forcibly blown over it. In stagnant air the cylinder would create an aura of torrid air between and around the fins, and heat transfer from cylinder to surrounding atmosphere would be virtually killed. Therefore, in order to facilitate rapid heat dissipation and insure adequate cooling, the air cooled marine engine is equipped with a blower, usually machined right into the flywheel (Fig. 13).

Air is sucked into the center of the flywheel-type centrifugal blower, then blasted through a simple sheet metal duct and blown across the cylinder and head. The cylinder is fitted with a snug metal baffle to force cooling air

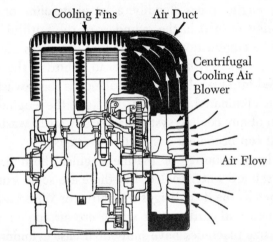

Cooling Fins   Air Duct

Centrifugal
Cooling Air
Blower

Air Flow

Fig. 13. *The temperature of an air-cooled engine is controlled by fresh air pumped over fins by the flywheel blower.*

all the way around the periphery, thus assuring that both sides will be equally cooled (or nearly so). With any cooling system, unequal cooling of the cylinder's opposite sides causes distorted thermal growth of metal, and the cylinder bore becomes egg-shaped.

Air cooling is not merely the process of blowing air over a cylinder in haphazard fashion. In a well designed air cooled engine the fins are scientifically designed and carefully placed so that the air stream will carry away maximum waste heat. The standard practice is to provide about 0.25 square feet of cooling fin area for each horsepower. For example, a four-horsepower engine will have about one square foot of cooling area.

Compared to a water cooled engine, the air cooled machine enjoys the advantages of extremely simple installation, there being no piping, hose, hull fittings or other cooling accessories to fuss with. Air cooling offers another advantage in eliminating small internal water passages which can become clogged with rust, mud or debris. Finally, it has the advantage of never freezing in winter. But there are disadvantages, naturally. Perhaps the greatest air cooling fault is the inability of the system to control hot-spot temperatures as well as water. Another drawback is that the air cooled motor must be mounted in the boat so that the heated air can blow freely away. And the last disadvantage of consequence is that power is wasted in driving the blower, power which would otherwise be available for propulsion.

An air cooled engine is cared for in very much the same way as a water cooled one. The cooling system is so simple that under ordinary circumstances it requires scant attention, but it is important to keep the air inlet clean and unobstructed because even a small patch of cleaning rag or a modest piece of paper could block the flow of air and perhaps ruin the engine. The sheet metal duct and cylinder baffle should be checked occasionally to make certain that they are positioned correctly and secured tightly in place, and, of course, to make sure that there is no obstruction which might reduce air volume.

The two most important points to observe when installing an air cooled motor are 1. provide plenty of breezy
fresh air, and 2. select a propeller that will let the engine
spin at full rated speed. If the motor is cooped up in a
stuffy engine box, the ambient temperature will rise so
high that the machine will soon roast to death, and of
course there is danger of fire from such elevated temperatures. Propeller diameter and pitch should be chosen
so that the engine can spin fast enough for the cooling
blower to operate efficiently. It is obvious that an oversize
propeller will cause overheating forthwith, and it is also
apparent that an air cooled engine is more sensitive to
propeller selection than is a water cooled one. The air
cooled engine's exhaust pipe operates at near-red heat;
therefore, as a fire precaution, it must be installed with
adequate heat insulation from wooden parts and should
be arranged so that the crew cannot accidentally be
burned by it.

A basic marine engine water cooling system consists
of a pump, the necessary piping plus a system of water
passages and jackets throughout the engine. The pump
sucks water from outside the hull and forces it up to the
engine where it is circulated and piped overboard, usually out of the exhaust pipe. The reason for dumping the
expended cooling water into the exhaust pipe is that the
water cools the feverish pipe and also helps quiet the engine's throaty roar.

One typical marine cooling system works like this:
water is pumped to the engine by a bronze gear pump
driven at engine speed from the tail shaft of the generator. The cool water is sent into the water jackets which run

the full length of the cylinders, thence to the jackets around the valve region, through the cylinder head and combustion chamber jackets, into the exhaust manifold jacket, then out the exhaust pipe to be dumped unceremoniously overboard.

Most modern engines, both gasoline and diesel, and some outboards, have a thermostat to control cooling water temperature (Figs. 14 and 15). When the engine is cold the thermostat positions a by-pass valve so that water is re-circulated through the system and a little cold sea water is drawn in. As the engine warms its innards, the thermostat starts to admit cold sea water to dilute the hot water in the system and to control the temperature. Temperature control is quite important because chilly operation can hurt an engine almost as much as overheating. Sub-normal cooling water temperature robs power and causes rapid formation of gum and sludge within the engine.

Many modern marine engines are equipped with an oil cooler which is essentially a heat exchanger. The engine's crankcase lubricating oil is pumped through a coil of copper tubing, situated inside a small water tank through which cold water is pumped; consequently the oil is cooled (Fig. 16). Some engines have a separate thermostat to control oil temperature by regulating the flow of coolant or lubricant through the cooler. Other engines, such as the Chrysler Ace, combine the oil cooler and oil filter into one convenient unit. On many engines the oil cooler incorporates a by-pass valve which operates in the event the cooler becomes clogged. If there is a stoppage in the exchanger, the valve simply removes the cooler

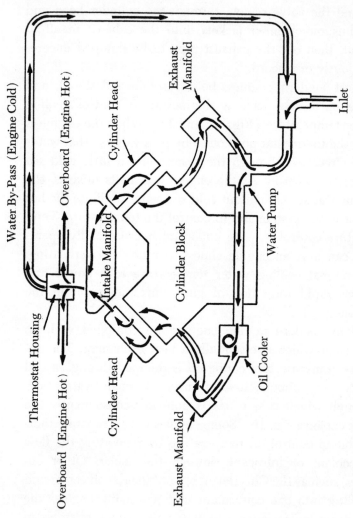

Fig. 14. *This drawing shows that the thermostat recirculates warm water back through the system when the engine is cool.*

from the oil circuit and the balance of the lubricating system continues to operate normally.

Why does a marine engine require an oil cooler when an automobile engine does not?

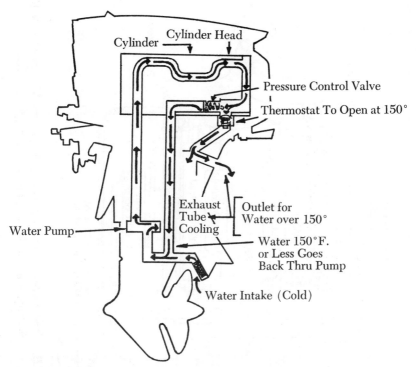

Fig. 15. *The thermostatically controlled cooling system of an Evinrude outboard motor.*

There are two reasons: The marine engine works considerably harder for its size than an automobile engine, consequently the lubrication system is required to carry away much more heat from bearings, cylinders, pistons

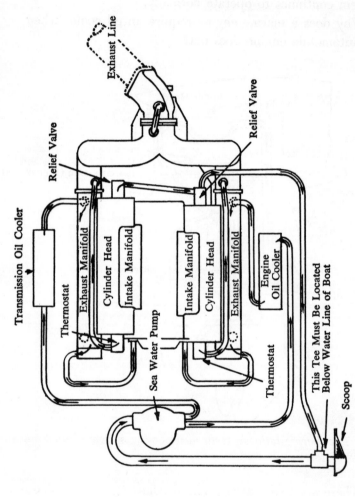

Fig. 16. *Raw sea water cooling system of a modern V-8 marine engine. The cool water is first warmed by being pumped through oil coolers.*

and other lubricated surfaces. Also, the automobile engine operates in a turbulent breeze of fresh air which naturally cools the oil in the crankpan. The marine engine, on the other hand, sits in a small box of hot, stagnant air and enjoys little or no cooling from the steamy air in the bilge.

Oil coolers generally require little attention or service. If the cooler is the combination type incorporating a cleaner element, it should be unbuttoned and the element replaced about every one hundred hours of operation. Any other type cooler should be removed from the engine and given a thorough flush with dry cleaning solvent once every two or three years because sludge is more likely to form on the cool surfaces of the heat exchanger than in any other place in the engine.

One of the obvious differences between the cooling system on an automobile engine and that on a marine engine is the large water jacket on the exhaust manifold of the marine unit. How come?

The answers are almost identical to those on the oil cooler question. The marine engine works much harder than the car engine with the result that exhaust gases are hotter and rush through the manifold in greater volume. Also, the marine engine operates in still air and lacks the blast of fan-created wind to cool the manifold, hence without water cooling the cast iron would be heated to incandescence. Such feverish temperatures are harmful to engine components and cannot be tolerated on a boat because of the fire hazard, not to mention blistered paint and brightwork.

An appreciable number of engines use fresh water

cooling as a means of keeping corrosive salt water out of the engine's innards. A fresh water system is quite like the cooling arrangement in a truck or automobile excepting that the radiator found on the land vehicle is replaced by a heat exchanger in the boat (Fig. 17). The cooling arrangement is a closed circuit and the same charge of fresh water is circulated 'round and 'round from engine to cooler and back again. Several types of coolers are used.

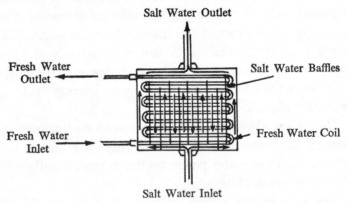

Fig. 17. *This schematic shows how a heat exchanger works in a fresh water cooling system.*

One type is similar to the oil cooler described earlier excepting that fresh coolant is circulated through the cooling coils while cold sea water is circulated through the tank (Fig. 18). This system requires two pumps: one to circulate the coolant through engine and heat exchanger while the other pump sucks up sea water and gushes it through the exchanger tank. The most common practice is to expel the sea or "raw" water out of the exhaust pipe to provide the craft with a wet exhaust.

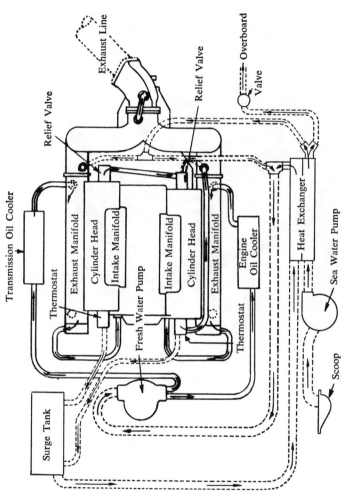

Fig. 18. *Fresh water cooling system for a powerful Gray V-8 marine engine. Note that salt water is pumped through the heat exchanger first.*

A different fresh water system uses a keel cooler or set of pipes fastened to the bottom of the hull (Fig. 19). This provides the simplest kind of heat exchanger and eliminates the raw water pump. However, it also eliminates the

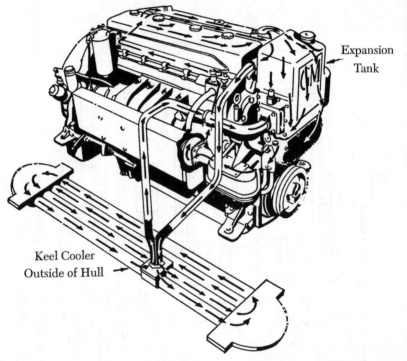

Fig. 19. *Fresh water cooling system in a General Motors diesel engine.*

advantages of a wet exhaust, in which case the first section of exhaust pipe is frequently provided with a water jacket to aid in controlling the temperature.

Fresh water cooling systems are provided with an expansion tank, generally of one or two gallons capacity and fitted with a filler cap. The position and function of the tank is the same as that of the header on top of an automobile or truck radiator: it provides space for the water to expand when heated, and contains a reserve to make up for evaporation and minor leakage.

In warm weather it is a good idea to pour a can of rust inhibitor into the fresh water, and in freezing weather it goes without saying that the system must either be drained or filled with anti-freeze mixture; either methanol or glycol may be used, same as in a car.

If you want to convert your salt water cooled engine to fresh water cooling, it is advisable to contact the engine manufacturer and tell him of your plans. Some manufacturers have a kit for the purpose, and in any event their recommendations and advice will be valuable. Most engines require a centrifugal fresh water pump to replace the gear or vane pump used with raw water cooling, and the engine manufacturer may be able to supply this pump or recommend one to purchase. Manufacturers of keel coolers and heat exchangers are competent to recommend the size and model for your particular engine.

Cooling system maintenance is generally quite simple and consists chiefly of keeping pipes and jackets clean and free of silt, keeping sea cocks operable, and lubricating the water pump at regular intervals. If your engine is fitted with a sand and trash trap, keep an eye on it and clean it as necessary. If you have had the bad luck to run aground, check as soon as you are re-floated to be sure that water is recirculating again and that the water intake hose has not collapsed from suction. When your engine is disassembled for overhaul, take off all water jacket clean-out plates and scrub the passages with a wire brush to remove scale, rust and silt. Use a scraper and stiff brush to clean rust from the small passages which run from block to head. If these passages become clogged and restrict water flow, steam pockets may form in the cylinder head.

If the water pump is belt driven, be sure that the belt is in good condition and tight enough to operate without slip. If the pump is driven by flexible coupling (rubber hose in some cases) be sure the coupling is not rotten. Keep the pump lubricated as specified in the engine handbook and take a peek at the shaft packing from time to time.

If you suspect that the thermostat is not working properly, it may be removed from its housing and tested with a pan of water heated to about 150 degrees Fahrenheit. Observe the length of the bellows or temperature element when the thermostat is cold, then dip it into the hot water for two minutes; the bellows should expand. Next, dip the assembly into cold tap water and the bellows should return to their original shape. Various thermostats have diverse design details, but the test may be applied to most of them.

After several years of use the engine water temperature gauge may well have its accuracy viewed with a jaundiced eye. If the old gauge claims that the engine is running too hot or too cold but the engine seems perfectly happy, it is a good idea to check the gauge before dickering with the engine. Carefully remove the bulb from the engine and dip it for two or three minutes in a pan of water heated to 150 degrees Fahrenheit (as verified by a good mercury thermometer). Naturally the engine meter should read about the same temperature. If it gives a wild reading, replace it. Another good check of actual engine temperature can be made by sticking the mercury thermometer through a rubber stopper and into the fitting from which the engine gauge was removed.

At laying up time in chilly climes, it is essential to completely drain every vestige of water from the cooling system. Open all the drain cocks, and as the water drains out, prod the openings with a piece of wire to be dead sure that silt has not clogged the drain before the last drop. An especially wise freeze-proofing measure is to close all the drains after purging the engine water and then fill the system with alcohol. The antifreeze will dilute any possible remaining pocket of water and prevent Jack Frost from doing his worst.

Chapter Four

HOW MARINE ENGINES
ARE LUBRICATED

THE MODERN marine engine is a pretty tough machine and will stand a lot of use and considerable abuse before cashing in its chips; but there is one maltreatment it will not tolerate: lack of oil.

You must lubricate your engine whether inboard or outboard, gasoline or diesel; you must lubricate it well or it will fail. Lube oil in the crankcase or mixed with the gasoline is the engine's life blood; allow this vital elixir to dry up, become foul or sludge ridden, and the engine is destined for trouble. In modern marine engines, particularly high speed ones, bearings, pistons and gears operate under high pressure and fast rubbing velocity. These parts are prevented from tearing asunder by a thin, almost microscopic, film of lubricating oil. As long as the film of oil is present, all is well with the engine, but allow that film to be destroyed and the engine will disintegrate.

The demands of the lubrication system upon the maintenance man are small, indeed. All that need be done is to keep the crankcase and clutch full of clean, high quality oil of correct viscosity, or, in the outboard, add the correct quantity of oil to the gasoline. A few minutes spent in changing an oil filter and greasing a few accessories can add untold hours to the useful life of a marine engine.

The function of engine lubrication is to reduce friction between moving parts, and oil is utilized to minimize friction not only because friction wastes power, but also because friction is destructive itself and creates searing heat. In accordance with the law of conservation of energy, all work that goes into overcoming friction in a bearing is turned into heat. Therefore, it is obvious that the more friction in a bearing, the more energy wasted, the hotter the bearing will become. An automobile brake is comparable to a tight, unlubricated bearing. When the brake is applied, friction between brake drum and band is terrific and all the kinetic energy of the speeding car is converted into heat within the brake assembly. In the brake the balance between mechanical work and heat is perfect; it must be, just as in a bearing.

A bearing completely deprived of lubrication may burn, fuse or seize in a weldment if conditions permit. If lubrication is inadequate or interrupted for a short time, the bearing may only be damaged or scored, but in any case it is lubrication alone which makes the use of journal bearings possible in gasoline and diesel engines. The new, powerful, high-speed, V-8 marine engines have scientific alloys in their bearing shells, alloys which are designed to stand up under fierce pounding, but even these tough bearings will disintegrate in seconds if deprived of oil. Some modern outboard motors make liberal use of ball and roller bearings. It is true that these bearings require scant lubrication, but nevertheless the pistons of a ball bearing motor need adequate lubrication, hence it is vital

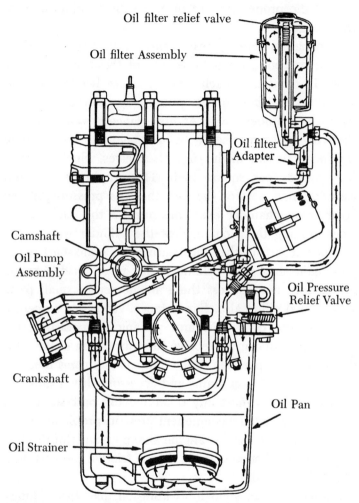

Fig. 20. *Cross-section diagram of the lubrication system in a gasoline marine engine.*

to add the proper amount of oil to the gasoline used in these engines.

Lubrication between piston and cylinder must be effective to prevent scoring or seizure of these parts as they move in relation to each other, because friction is quite severe on the faces of the piston rings where they bear upon the cylinder walls. At first glance it would appear that ring pressures should be low, being no greater than the spring tension of the rings themselves, which is only a few pounds per square inch. This would be a sound assumption if not for the fact that gas pressures in the combustion chamber exert pressure on the back of the rings, forcing them out against the cylinder walls.

While it is true that the bearings on crankshaft, wrist pins, cam shaft and cylinder walls must receive prime lubrication, nevertheless there are numerous small parts which need oiling also. For instance, valve stems operate under severe conditions and varying temperatures for long periods and must receive full lubrication every minute of engine operation. Valve tappets and cams must be oiled. All gears, gear trains and accessory drives must be bathed in oil as must any other moving part subject to friction. Each engine component presents problems which must be solved by the engine designer and lubrication engineer together so that the demon friction can be foiled (Figs. 20 and 21).

Primarily, then, good lubricating oil does three things for your engine: It reduces friction, retards heat generation and prevents wear of bearing surfaces. In addition to acting as lubricant, crankcase oil also plays the part of coolant by absorbing heat from hot engine surfaces

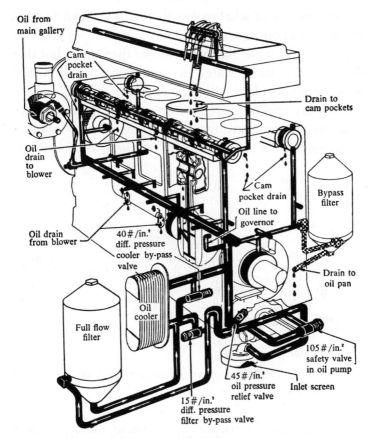

Fig. 21. *Schematic diagram of the lubricating system in a General Motors Series 71 marine diesel.*

and rejecting the heat by crankcase radiation and through the oil cooler provided on many modern gasoline and diesel marine engines (Fig. 22).

In considering how lubrication actually makes life smoother for the engine, it is interesting to examine the classic concept of what makes things "skid," and to think of dry friction, greasy friction and viscous friction. There may be more glamorous names than these, but they describe the three states or conditions of lubrication which can take place within an engine component.

With dry friction there are two surfaces in actual molecular contact, one moving over the other with no lubricant between. The automobile brake employs dry friction to

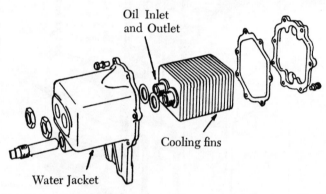

Oil Inlet
and Outlet

Cooling fins

Water Jacket

Fig. 22. *Exploded view of an oil cooler used on a Chrysler marine engine.*

advantage, and the friction is, of course, enormous for a given unit pressure on the surfaces. No engine bearing, not even a ball bearing, can exist for long under the condition of dry friction.

When two metal surfaces are moving in relation to each other, virtually in contact, and yet are actually lubricated with some substance which eases their travel and discourages mutual adhesion, the laws of "greasy" friction apply. Under these conditions friction is much less than with dry friction, however great loads or speeds may not be borne on surfaces depending upon this type lubrication. "Greasy" friction does not imply any reference to grease. It is a word defining the kind of friction which may take place with even the least viscous kind of oil, provided the film of lubricant is not dimensionally thick enough to physically separate the two surfaces. "Greasy" friction might apply to a tight nut, the turning being made easier by a drop of oil. It is certain that the nut would not be floating on oil, yet it would undoubtedly turn easier than with dry threads.

Viscous friction is in effect when two adjacent surfaces are completely separated from each other by a film of lubricant. Naturally, this type of friction is the most desirable, and fortunately it is the kind of friction dealt with in almost every moving part of a marine engine. All engine journal bearings are completely oil borne, as are the pistons, rings, wrist pins and cam shaft bearings. When a journal bearing is lubricated correctly, the rotating shaft is floated on a film of oil such that the surfaces of the two parts never come in contact. The thickness of oil film can only be measured in micro-inches, but nevertheless the metal surfaces never touch.

A journal bearing operating correctly in an oil borne state, helps maintain its own oil film by wedging action (Fig. 23). The vital oil film which separates the two surfaces is partly maintained by this wedging action due to the fact that the spinning shaft sets itself eccentrically in its bearing; the boundary layer of oil tends to adhere to the rotating shaft, is dragged around by the revolving shaft and forced into the narrow space which separates

the surfaces. In this connection it is interesting to note that
a bearing which handles a combination oscillating and
rotating load has the ability to hold a lubricant film better than a bearing of equal size supporting a constant,
unidirectional load. By the time the oil on one side of
the bearing has been pressed thin by loading, the thrust
is reversed, pulling the shaft over to the other side where

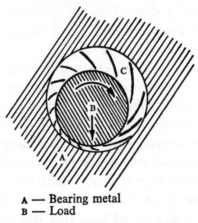

A — Bearing metal
B — Load

Fig. 23. *A much exaggerated diagram to illustrate how lubricated surfaces are separated by the wedging action of the oil.*

the oil film is thicker; consequently the shaft is always
shifting from thin to thick layer of lubricant. Prime example of a bearing which operates under reversing load
is a connecting rod big-end bearing.

There are numerous factors which tend to alter the di-
mensional thickness of oil film in a bearing, the foremost
being change in viscosity of the oil itself. Since reduction
of viscosity reduces the thickness of oil film, and since
increase of temperature reduces viscosity, it follows that

increased heat in the bearing tends to make the lubricating film scanty. Increased load decreases the thickness of oil film by simply squeezing out the lubricant like a baker's rolling pin on soft dough. Increase of shaft speed has two opposite effects. First, higher speed increases film thickness by stepping up wedging activity. Second, it decreases film thickness as follows: As the shaft spins

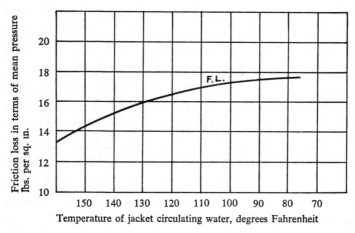

Fig. 24. *Running an engine too cool wastes power because viscous friction increases as water temperature decreases.*

faster, shearing of the oil, or viscous friction, becomes greater, increasing the heat thrown into the bearing. The resulting heat reduces viscosity with consequent reduction of film thickness (Fig. 24). The net result of the two changes would about cancel if not for the fact that in a marine bearing loads increase with speed, thus the ultimate result is reduction of film thickness.

If a journal bearing or other bearing surface such as

the piston wall is overloaded to such an extent that the oil film is broken down, the adjacent surfaces come in contact and the laws of greasy friction begin to apply. If overloading or insufficient lubrication persists, there is serious danger of the bearing surfaces being scored or burned. This is one reason why manufacturers advise "breaking-in" a marine engine gently. When new, even the best fitted bearings, pistons and cams have minute irregularities and high spots which can bridge the protective oil film and create a tiny hot spot. Once the film is broken down and local heating occurs, there can be a chain reaction brought about by friction leading to heat, heat lowering viscosity, lowered viscosity reducing film thickness, and reduced thickness causing more friction and heat. . . . This vicious circle can ruin an engine.

Breaking in an engine slowly assures that tiny high spots on bearing surfaces break through the oil film less often, and do little harm when bridging the film. As the engine wears in, the high spots are erased and the bearings are ready for full duty.

Marine engines manufactured in the past decade require much less running in than older models because engineering methods have been perfected to give friction surfaces smoother, shinier finishes with fewer high spots. Bearing journals, valve stems, cams and cylinder walls are honed by scientific methods until they have mirror-like surfaces, smooth to within a few micro inches. Unbelievable as it sounds, surfaces have actually been honed so fantastically smooth that they were actually poorer bearing surfaces than rougher ones. Microscopic observations by lubrication engineers revealed that the surfaces were so flawless and glazed that they could retain no oil film, hence from the practical standpoint such ultra finishing was not desirable where good lubrication was a factor. However, modern production micro-finishing renders just the desired smoothness.

Fascinating experiments are being conducted using air for a lubricant in bearings of ultra fast spinning shafts which operate with tiny clearance between shaft and bearing. Air is pumped into the bearing under high pressure, and the wedging action causes the shaft to float in the bearing. However, to date there is no application for such technique in the house-cat marine engine.

If a spinning shaft is completely oil borne there is no apparent reason for the mating parts to wear at all, since there is no metal-to-metal friction. Indeed, it is true that the bearings would not wear at all if not for the abrasive action of microscopic particles of grit, dust and carbon carried in the oil; particles which are usually too small to be removed by ordinary filters. These minute particles of foreign matter are carried to the bearings by the very lubricant which they contaminate. Bearing wear is caused like this: The oil carries tiny particles of grit into the bearings; part of the grit embeds in the softer of the two metals, the bearing sleeve or shell. Once the grit has become embedded in the soft metal, it proceeds to grind away the hard metal of the shaft.

Of course only the larger particles of grit are able to span the oil film and cause wear, which is another reason why a dimensionally thicker oil film reduces bearing wear. Because the abrasive particles are embedded in the softer of the two metals, it is the steel shaft of the harder of the metals which is worn most. Knowing this, marine engine manufacturers use the hardest possible steel for the crankshaft to help it resist abrasion, and they use as soft a metal as practical for the bearing shell so that grit can bury itself easily and do no harm. Some marine engines have crankshafts with the journals especially hardened by newly invented methods so that the surface metal is almost glass hard and the interior metal is tough and ductile.

From an abrasion standpoint, the worst possible combination is a soft shaft rotating in relatively hard bearing metal. For example, a soft bronze shaft revolving in a babbit bearing will wear so rapidly that it is almost unbelievable.

The embedded grit theory offers an answer to why cylinders wear at different rates. It has been observed that cylinders wear faster with aluminum pistons than with cast iron ones, yet it is the cylinders which wear more rapidly, not the pistons. This is logical. The aluminum pistons are much softer than the iron ones, therefore pick up and retain more embedded grit which grinds against the cylinder walls. In comparison, cast iron pistons are harder and carry less grit, also, they are approximately the same hardness as the cylinders so that wear is more equal.

Marine engineers recognize that dirty oil causes rapid bearing wear, so they provide most modern inboard engines with efficient oil filters. These filters are a great help in reducing engine wear, but in order to do an efficient job, the filter element must be changed often. It is hard to establish a set rule on frequency of filter element change for all engines, but most manufacturers suggest about every 100 hours of operation. Naturally, the oil should be changed when the filter is serviced.

We have heard it argued by knowledgeable boating folks that there is no need ever to change crankcase oil because the oil never wears out, and because even if gasoline should dilute the oil the fuel will eventually evaporate anyway.

But this argument is weak: Oil does not wear out nor lose its lubricating properties, but it gets just plain dirty and acidy and should be changed as a normal procedure in preventive maintenance. Simply adding fresh oil to replenish that which is consumed does not take out the dirt, and even the best filters cannot remove all traces of dirt and acid. The only way to remove all foreign matter is to pump the crankcase dry and refill it with clean oil at regular intervals.

Crankcase oil in inboard gasoline and diesel engines not only becomes contaminated by carbon and dust, but also picks up acid, an acid which can do considerable harm by etching metal engine parts and accelerating the formation of sludge or varnish. Acid appears in the oil mainly as a result of cold engine starts. Appreciable quantities of water condense in the crankcase and combine with sulphur compounds from the fuel and lubricating oil to form an acid. Engines which are subjected to frequent cold starts, engines which operate with cooling systems too chilly, and those which are used only for short runs are most susceptible to acid damage and should have most frequent oil changes.

How frequently should oil be changed? There is no hard

and fast rule, but most engine makers suggest a change every 100 hours of operation. An engine used in cool, damp weather with frequent cold starts probably would be happier with a change every fifty hours. Generally speaking, closer attention to oil changes should be accorded the diesel more than the gasoline engine because

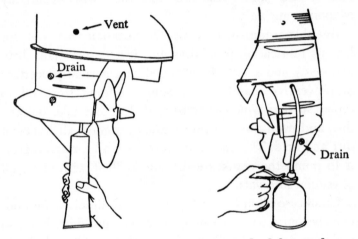

Fig. 25. *Outboard motor lower units must be lubricated regularly.*

diesel fuel oils tend to have more sulphur content than gasoline, and traces of sulphur invite acid formation.

The outboard motor is beautifully free of oil change problems because lube oil is added to the gasoline and is being constantly changed as it is burned after use. Most outboard motors are lubricated by adding one half pint of S.A.E. No. 30 engine oil to one gallon of gasoline, therefore when the motor has run long enough to consume eight gallons of fuel, it has enjoyed an automatic two quart oil change.

Marine diesel engine manufacturers usually recommend oil changes at 100 hour intervals and they further recommend the use of highly detergent, heavy duty lubricants. Frequent oil changes are especially important in diesels because of the sulphur content in the fuel. Concerning oil filtration, General Motors has the following to say in reference to the series "71" marine diesel: "Heavy sludge deposits found on the oil filter elements at the time of an oil change must be taken as an indication that the detergency of the oil has been exhausted. When this occurs, the oil drain interval should be shortened. The removal of abrasive dust, metal particles, and carbon must be ensured by replacement of the oil filter elements at the time of oil change."

General Motors and other diesel manufacturers recommend the use of heavy duty oil meeting the specifications of Military Spec. MIL-L-2104A, S-1 and Series 3. A list of brand names meeting these requirements may be had by writing to Internal Combustion Engine Institute, 201 North Wells Street, Chicago 6, Illinois.

On most marine engines, all basic operating parts are lubricated by the crankcase oil, but there usually are accessories which must be lubricated separately with oil can or grease gun (Fig. 25). On an outboard motor, the most important lubricating job is the lower unit; it just cannot receive too much attention because it operates in a tough spot—underwater. In spite of grease seals and other built-in devices, water frequently finds its

way into the lower unit of an outboard, and needless to
say steel gears do not relish water, particularly salt water.
Some lower units are lubricated by a special grease made
specifically for the purpose and sold in oversized toothpaste tubes, and some are lubricated by gear oil. The engine manual will specify what lubricant to use; the important point is to follow instructions and lubricate this
vulnerable mechanism frequently.

On inboard engines, both gasoline and diesel, the reduction gears and clutches are frequently lubricated
separately from the engine, and some reduction gear units
have their own oil cooler separate from the cooler provided for the engine. These machines are usually lubricated with the same grade oil as the engine crankcase,
but in some instances automotive automatic transmission
oil is used to discourage foaming. Oil changes are required only once a year on most separate systems because
there is very little chance for the lubricant to become contaminated.

Most marine engines, both inboard and outboard,
have accessories which require manual lubrication. Most
ignition distributors have a little felt oil wick at the center
of the shaft, under the plastic rotor arm (Fig. 26). The
felt should be saturated with a few drops of oil once every
100 hours. The base of the distributor usually has an oil
or grease cup; this should be given a drop of oil or a half
turn (if grease cup) once every twenty-five hours. Most
generators have one or two oil cups for the armature bearings; these should be given a shot of engine oil every 250
hours (Fig. 27).

Tachometer cables frequently disintegrate to a rusty

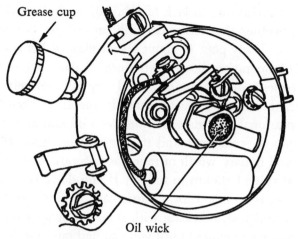

Grease cup

Oil wick

Fig. 26. *The distributor oil wick should receive a few drops of oil every hundred hours and the grease cup should be given a half-turn every 25 hours.*

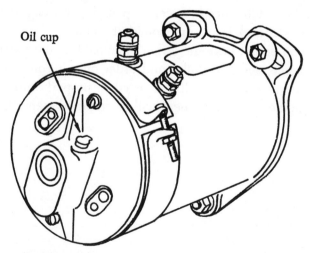

Oil cup

Fig. 27. *The generator oil cup should be given a drop or two of oil every 250 hours.*

mass of metal due to lack of lubrication. Prevent this by disconnecting the cable assembly up at the instrument end and slowly pour in about a shot glass of light-bodied oil. This operation should be performed about once a year.

Frequent diligent use of the oil can will also help keep choke, throttle and clutch controls operating cheerfully. An occasional Saturday morning with oil can and grease gun can do your boat and its engine more good than a thousand dollars' worth of fancy accessories. And there is a good rule of thumb to follow: If you don't know what lubricant is specified for a particular job, don't just let it go dry and rust, lubricate with some oil or grease to the best of your judgment until you can find out exactly what is specified. After all, any lubricant is better than letting the machine grind itself to a cinder.

Think carefully of what a famous engineer once said: "The total difference between a spanking new engine and a worn-out junk is just one pound of metal!"

If you do not have the owner's manual for your particular engine, spend a dollar and order one; it contains all the information you will ever need to properly lubricate the engine. Your investment will be returned many times.

Chapter Five

THE MARINE ENGINE'S
IGNITION SYSTEM

THE WEATHER was foul, the seas were choppy and the wet wind was blowing low scud fast across the horizon, when into the marina limped a cruiser, its engine coughing along on two or three cylinders and its skipper frantically dickering with the carburetor. At last the boat was nursed into a slip and the engine died with a sickening gasp.

"Carburetor trouble, serious carburetor trouble," moaned the distraught owner to the competent looking mechanic who appeared on the scene. "Fix the carburetor and we'll be able to shove off on our cruise."

The mechanic said nothing, bent over the engine, ignored the carburetor completely, went straight to the distributor, adjusted the breaker points and then snapped the cap back smartly on the distributor.

"Now start the engine," he directed quietly.

The puzzled owner touched the starter button and could hardly get his finger off the switch quick enough as the engine roared into action. "But," he fussed, red faced, "everything pointed to carburetor trouble; I was certain she wasn't getting gas!"

"Yes, that's usually the way," smiled the professional

trouble-shooter, "but long ago I learned a single sentence which has guided my engine doctoring like a religion: 'When everything points to carburetor trouble, go straight to the ignition.' That philosophy became almost a fetish with me."

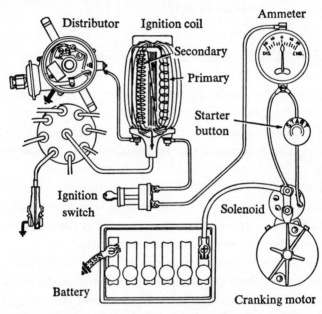

Fig. 28. *Diagram of the complete ignition system.*

The aftermath of the little tale is that the ignition was fixed in minutes, but it took the competent, philosophic mechanic the better part of an hour to put the carburetor back in operating trim after it had been doctored by unkind hands.

Now, it would be foolish to say that the fuel systems on marine engines never give trouble or that carburetors do not become clogged or maladjusted, but the frequency of such trouble is certainly less than that experienced with the ignition system. This is surely not a rap at the quality of ignition furnished on inboard or outboard engines. There is nothing basically wrong with the machinery, it is simply that electrons and water do not get along well together. Ten thousand volts and dampness mix as smoothly as dogs and cats in the same cage. Ignition wiring handles voltage in excess of ten thousand, and obviously a boat engine is subjected to the most miserable dampness, therefore conditions are ripe for trouble.

It is an interesting fact that repeated drenching dampness alternated with dry spells is worse on electrical gear than total water immersion. The armed services are aware of this and have devised specifications for laboratory testing of electrical equipment, such tests comprising cycles of extreme humidity alternated with dry spells and heat. In some instances the electrical equipment is subjected to hot and cold salt water spray. Such torture tests are terribly tough on electrical machinery, and specimens frequently fail to pass, but just think for a moment that your boat subjects electrical accessories to much the same punishment. Is it any wonder that the ignition system requires a little attention and understanding? (Fig. 28.)

If the ignition system is the nervous system of the engine, then the distributor is the brain and coordinates the activities of the other components (Fig. 29). The lower section of the distributor accurately times the spark to a precise instant and automatically advances and retards the timing in accordance with engine speed and load. In the upper section of the distributor the high vol-

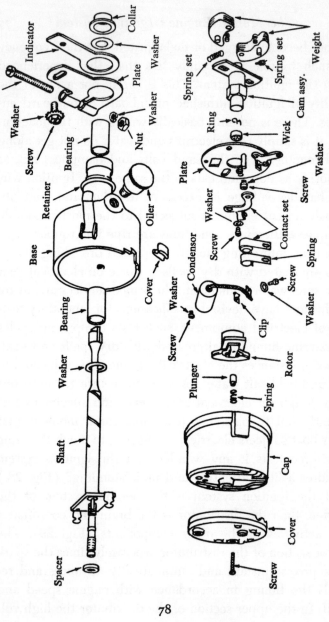

Fig. 29. *Exploded view of a complete distributor.*

tage is routed to the correct spark plug in accordance with the firing order of the cylinders. In a speeding engine the sequence is repeated so rapidly as to be a blur to the eye, and yet exact timing must be assured through all conditions.

The actual pulses of spark are minutely timed by the

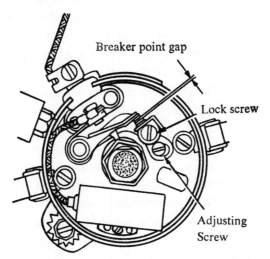

Fig. 30. *View of a distributor with the cap removed. The breaker points are shown in the full open position.*

points. The points are a simple, cam operated, single pole switch which is normally held closed by spring pressure and pushed open by a rotating multi-lobed cam which rotates at half engine speed. Spark flashes at the exact instant the points open or separate, not when they close (Fig. 30).

High voltage for the spark is actually generated within the spark coil. The coil is a straightforward transformer having a primary and secondary winding both wound around a laminated iron core and having rugged insulation to withstand pulses of high voltage, voltage which may exceed fifteen thousand under some circumstances.

The third important electrical component in the spark generating apparatus is the condenser or capacitor (two words for the same animal). The capacitor is wired across the points so that it charges when the points are open and discharges when they are closed. The condenser might be thought of as a tiny, high voltage storage battery (which it is not, technically) capable of being quickly charged and discharged, hence at the instant the points "break" the condenser is empty and it absorbs a surge or charge and helps prevent the points from burning due to excess current. However, the more important function of the capacitor is to cause "ringing" or resonance in the winding of the ignition coil and jack up the voltage in the secondary winding. The ignition system will operate weakly without the condenser, but the spark will be so anemic that it will not jump the spark plug electrodes.

Here is how the points, coil and capacitor function together to generate high ignition voltage: The points are closed to allow battery voltage (6 or 12 volts) to flow through the few turns of primary winding in the coil. Because the coil is wound around an iron core the current flow builds up a healthy magnetic flux. At this stage the condenser is shorted out by the points and is completely discharged. Suddenly, the points snap open and interrupt the flow of battery current through the primary winding; with the current flow chopped off there is nothing to support the magnetic field in the iron core and the field collapses in a flash. The collapsing lines of force cut across the thousands of fine wire turns in the secondary winding and induce a great voltage. At this time the condenser has been thrown in series with the primary winding and receives a surge of current from the collapsing field and acts like an electrical "spring" bouncing voltage back and forth between itself and the coil. This "ringing" or resonance further builds up the voltage in the secondary in jagged peaks or pulses which can be viewed on the screen of an oscilloscope or ignition analyzer.

After the voltage has died down and the engine has rotated, the ignition points close again and a new magnetic field is created in the core of the coil. A small voltage is actually produced in the coil at the instant of point closing, but because the core saturates relatively slowly the voltage is negligible.

Hot spark surges through the ignition system only when the three basic components are in top condition. The points must be adjusted to correct gap, must be clean, and must be snapped shut by a strong spring. The capacitor must be of correct value and not "lossy." The coil must have good continuity in both windings and must be free of high voltage leaks.

Of the three components, the points require the most attention because they are continually beaten by mechanical as well as electrical shocks. If the contact faces of the points become burned and pitted, a high resistance connection may result and will cause hard starting, poor idling and missing at high speed. Poor point contact means that the coil is not fully saturated and that the field collapses slowly, resulting in low spark voltage at the plugs.

Point gap clearance, the distance between point surfaces when fully open, is quite important. If the adjustment is made too small, the points do not open positively with a snap and the spark voltage may be low and uncertain, particularly at slow engine speeds. If the clearance is too great, the points are open most of the time and the coil does not have time to saturate at high speed. Consequently, excess point clearance is a cause of faulty ignition at high engine speed.

The points are closed by spring pressure and maintenance of full pressure is important for two reasons: First, if pressure is too slight, electrical contact is uncertain and ignition voltage will be weak or dead. Second, and most important, the points open and close very rapidly in a high speed engine. They are pushed open forcibly by a rotating cam and cannot lag behind at opening, but if the spring is weak and cannot overcome inertia of the points, they will not close in time to saturate the coil, and ignition will be ragged. Weak point springs will cause an engine to miss and surge and buck at very high speed. Weak spring and excessive point clearance together will severely limit top speed of an engine.

A faulty condenser can be spotted in two ways: Frequently, it will cause rapid burning of the points and will always cause weak, anemic looking spark. It is impractical to repair a condenser; if one acts suspicious it should be replaced.

A faulty ignition coil will usually have a broken primary or secondary winding or will be electrically leaky at the high voltage insulator. If the insulator is cracked or defective there may be a conductive path from the "hot" terminal to ground and a visible spark will jump to the case or low voltage terminals. Incidentally, it is very hard on a coil to snap the ignition points while testing for spark unless the high voltage wire is close enough to "ground" to allow the jumping of a spark. If the high voltage circuit of the coil is left open, the spark has no place to jump and may arc inside the coil and ruin the insulation.

Other things being equal, the longer the gap which the spark is forced to jump, the higher will be the spark voltage. This is the basis of some spark "intensifiers" on the market; they are simply a spark gap. The devices do what is claimed, but they are tough on the ignition system. Sometimes a temporary additional gap may be used to advantage in trouble shooting. If one cylinder is dead due to a fouled spark plug, it may sometimes be rejuvenated by holding the high voltage wire about a quarter inch from the plug terminal so as to increase the voltage at the plug tips.

So far we have examined the components which generate the high spark voltage, but how does the "juice" get from the coil to the spark plugs?

There is a single high voltage wire at one end of the coil which transmits the spark from coil back to distributor. The center terminal on the distributor cap receives this wire and carries the spark through a conductor in the cap to the rotor which spins around on the end of the shaft. The rotor is a rapid rotary switch which transmits the spark to small metal contacts molded into the distributor cap, thence the spark goes into the high voltage wires leading to the plugs.

The distributor cap and rotor are simple in construction and function, but because they handle the full voltage and must transmit it without loss, they require some maintenance. Should the distributor cap be cracked, the voltage will follow moisture in the crack, ground out the spark and kill the engine. If the cap becomes excessively damp it will kill the spark. Should it get dirty or carbonized it will strangle the spark effectively. Ignition maintenance should include periodic wiping of the distributor cap with carbon tetrachloride or perclene or, even better, a silicone compound such as Dow-Corning 200 Compound or equivalent. Automotive supply stores and electronic supply houses sell electrical grade silicone compounds as viscous liquids, greases and sprays. A trace of this material rubbed as a polish on the distributor cap both inside and out will work wonders in preventing moisture from killing engine performance. Similarly, a thin coat should be applied to the distributor rotor and to all high voltage wiring as well as to the entire outside surface of the spark plugs and the exterior of the ignition coil. Indeed, a thin coat of silicone compound polished on all electrical accessories makes them look nice and discourages rust.

Many outboard motors are sparked by magneto ignition instead of by coil and distributor. The underlying principles of operation are exactly the same except that primary current is obtained from a permanent magnet generator incorporated as part of the unit. The points, capacitor and coil perform the same function, and maintenance is similar (Fig. 31).

Some inboard marine engines are equipped with magneto and these mags usually have an impulse coupling to provide hot starting spark. Since a magneto depends upon engine rotation to develop its voltage, the spark would be weak at cranking speed unless special provi-

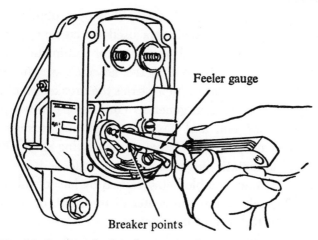

Fig. 31. *Setting the breaker point clearance in a magneto.*

sions were made to increase the voltage. An impulse coupling holds back the rotor of the magneto until the piston is at top center, then at the correct instant the coupling snaps the rotor ahead at high speed so that an intense, hot spark is generated. The impulse mechanism is disengaged as soon as the engine starts and it then serves as a conventional drive.

In general, magneto ignition is highly reliable and is

independent of the boat's electrical system. Magneto spark is usually very hot, and the voltage increases as engine speed goes up, whereas distributor spark usually becomes weaker at high speeds—the very time that the best spark is needed. Most magnetos are made with high quality parts and a nice attention to workmanship, hence are relatively expensive compared to the ordinary coil and distributor.

The hand operated spark control has been obsolete for some time and the distributors used on current marine engines use a centrifugal governor for automatic spark control. On most distributors the advance weights are located under the plate which carries the breaker point assembly. The mechanism generally consists of two weights pivoted at one end and having springs and linkage to adjust the cam position relative to the driving shaft (Fig. 32). The automatic advance requires little or no maintenance; the only trouble being caused by lack of lubrication on the felt pad at the center of the shaft, or by dirt getting into the weight mechanism.

The most important tune-up procedure on the ignition system is to correctly time the distributor or magneto so that spark occurs at precisely the correct instant.

Timing procedures vary from engine to engine and the maintenance manual must be consulted for details of timing marks, recommended settings, method of adjustment and specific precautions. However, there are remarks which apply in general:

There is always some backlash in the distributor drive, and when the engine is being turned slowly by hand to get the points just barely at the "break" point, it is advisable to put gentle hand torque on the distributor rotor against the direction of rotation. The exact instant of point separation (the instant of ignition) is easily determined by putting a small light bulb or voltmeter in series with

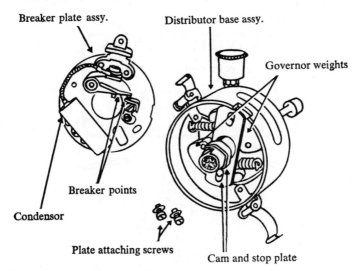

Fig. 32. *A distributor with the breaker plate removed to show the governor weights which control automatic advance.*

the low voltage wire running to the distributor. Ignition is advanced or made earlier by rotating the distributor body opposite the direction of rotor rotation; retarding the setting is done by rotating the distributor body with rotor rotation. After any adjustment is made, the hold-down screws must be firmly secured so that the timing will not be altered by engine vibration.

A timing light is very useful in adjusting spark because the setting may be checked while the engine is running, a more meaningful check than the static reading. Essentially, a timing light is a neon type light which flashes brightly every time a plug fires (Fig. 33). It is a simple stroboscope aimed at the timing marks, and the flash of

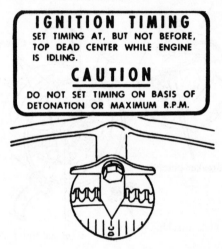

Fig. 33. *Flywheel timing marks on a powerful Chrysler V-8 marine engine.*

light is so quick that the flywheel or other rotating member carrying the timing marks appears to stand still at the instant of ignition. With a timing light the ignition may be checked at various speeds to assure that the automatic advance is operating within tolerances. For example, Chrysler specifies the following advance pattern for both the Ace and Crown M-46 and M-47:

Degree of Advance	Engine R.P.M.
0 deg.	700
6 deg.	800
10 deg.	1,400
14 deg.	2,000
18 deg.	2,600

After spark timing has been set using timing marks, it may be further checked by operating the engine under service conditions. If the engine is supplied with the proper grade gasoline and knocks or detonates at advanced throttle, the spark should be retarded just sufficiently to kill the pinging. However, should the engine knock or ping just a little as the throttle is opened suddenly for rapid acceleration, the spark is corrected and should not be retarded.

If the engine is running at correct temperature and is otherwise properly adjusted but tends to pop back through the carburetor air inlet, late spark is indicated and the distributor should be rotated to more advanced setting. Operating with excessively retarded spark causes high exhaust temperatures and is tough on valves; on the other hand, running with too much advance causes detonation, high pressures, and is tough on pistons, spark plugs and bearings. Ignition either too early or late wastes gasoline.

Manufacturers of modern, valve-in-head engines having compact, efficient combustion chambers have issued warnings against timing by "ear" utilizing detonation or knock as a criterion of advance. On many engines it is a practice to operate at full throttle, then advance spark timing until the engine knocks then retard just enough to squelch the ping. This usually gives a reasonable spark setting. However Palmer, Gray, Chrysler and others now warn that this timing method may be harmful to their efficient valve-in-head engines because the combustion chambers are so scientifically designed that detonation will not take place until the spark is harmfully far advanced. The companies urge that timing be accomplished carefully with reference to timing marks either statically or utilizing a timing light.

Ignition tune-up is facilitated by the use of an electronic ignition analyzer, a gadget which looks like a small television set and which hooks to the ignition wiring to present a picture of the spark pattern. Transport aircraft have used these machines for some years, but their thousand dollar cost prevented their use by amateur boating folks. However, there is one on the market now in kit form, a very respectable little instrument sold by Heathkit Co., Benton Harbor, Michigan. With this scope it is possible to locate malfunctions immediately and to compare the ignition on any engine with that of another engine at any speed or load.

Poor ignition performance can be caused by very simple things, things which are so easy to prevent that they are overlooked. Miserable, ratty wiring is a prime cause. If the high voltage wiring becomes aged and cracked, moisture will creep into the cracks and ground-out the spark; and unfortunately the moisture will do its worst exactly when you need all the spark you can muster to start a cold, dank engine. Good, fresh wires and a treatment of anti-moisture compound help a lot to start a cold, clammy engine. High resistance in the ignition switch or in the low voltage battery wiring can cause no end of trouble and is difficult to locate. This portion of the system may be checked out by putting a voltmeter across the system as shown in Fig. 34. If the wiring and switch are in

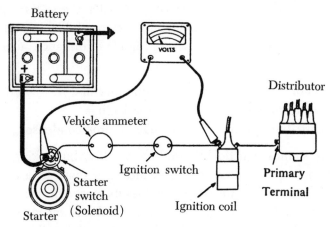

Fig. 34. *Resistance test of a primary ignition circuit. Breaker points must be closed when the test is made and the ignition switch must be "On."*

good shape the voltmeter should read less than a quarter volt, and preferably the voltage drop should be almost undetectable. (Be sure the ignition points are closed when performing the test.)

An inexpensive multi-meter which measures volts, ohms, current, is a wonderful aid in shooting trouble and maintaining the ignition system, indeed in doing any electrical work on the boat. An instrument adequate for work around engines may be purchased in an electronic supply house for about fifteen dollars, and several are available in kit form.

We are a nut on the subject of carrying spare parts for the ignition system, particularly on a single engined boat operating on anything larger than a lily pond. Several engine manufacturers offer a spare parts kit for their engines so that you do not have to order the parts separately. For example, Palmer includes the following items in the safety kit for their high performance model IH-240:

Set of breaker points	Ignition coil
Distributor cap	Spark plugs
Distributor rotor	Distributor condenser

It sounds a little like gilding the lily, but taking the ignition system home for the winter is a smart idea if the boat is to be laid up. Moisture does its most evil work during the cold, humid winter months, and it is not too much of a chore to remove the distributor and coil, or the magneto, to a nice, dry, warm house for the bleak months. While the system is residing comfortably in your centrally heated domicile you can install a new set of points and give it a thorough check-up in leisure and comfort.

Chapter Six

THE MARINE STORAGE BATTERY

THE MARINE storage battery is accurately compared to a mechanical flywheel because it absorbs power part of the time and delivers power to the system at alternate intervals. It is a powerful source of energy and a moderating influence on voltage fluctuations as well.

A modern storage battery is a strong, rugged component and if given nominal care will deliver faithful service for at least several seasons. Abused and neglected, it will fail or become inefficient after a short period of use, possibly after only a few hours. Battery abuse and lack of rudimentary care may result in shockingly steep bills, because even a small 12-volt automobile battery is an expensive item in these inflationary times. Contemporary batteries are well engineered, tough and powerful, but they require a sensible amount of attention. Preventive battery maintenance pays fat dividends; neglect costs hard earned cash.

Intelligent battery care is relatively simple and may be reduced to an easy routine. Even if you are ignorant of the primary principles underlying battery operation, you can intelligently service the component without much difficulty. But like other technical things, it is more fun and can be done more efficiently if you have an idea of what makes the battery tick.

First of all, let us define the term "storage battery" as used in this discussion: We are going to consider the lead-acid storage battery only, the house cat kind of battery used in automobiles, outboard motor starting and most

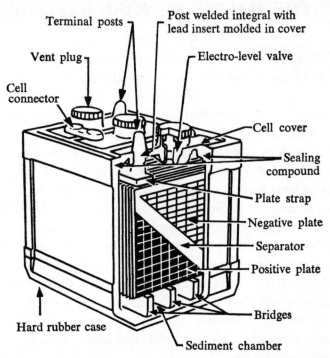

Fig. 35. *A Delco 6-volt storage battery with part of the case cut away.*

inboard powered boats (Fig. 35). We exclude dry batteries and also the Edison nickel-iron-alkaline storage battery. The reason for eliminating the Edison battery is not because it is inferior (indeed, it is superior in some respects) but because it is seldom used on moderate size boats. Hence, the fellow who tinkers with and maintains his own boat is not likely to encounter an Edison battery.

Basically, the battery in your boat is a device to store chemical (not electrical) energy, and to release the pent-up energy in electrical form when required. The really useful functions of the battery may be neatly put into two classes:

1. To provide electricity for cranking the engine, operating the ignition system, running lights, radios, fans and miscellaneous electrical equipment.

2. To provide a load for the generator and prevent excess voltage in the entire electrical system when the generator is operating.

The charging generator is actually the prime source of energy for the electrical system, but without a battery, generator power would be uncontrolled and unstable. In the first place, the generator, even if driven by auxiliary engine, could never furnish enough current to operate an electric starter; hence the main engine would have to be hand cranked if the boat lacked a battery. Secondly, a conventional engine-driven generator would deliver wildly fluctuating voltage if it were not for the battery's moderating influence. A storage battery floating in the circuit prevents voltage surges from burning out other electrical components and also protects the generator and generator control mechanism.

Suppose that you are working on the engine and the electrical system and that you make a complete electrical hook-up but omit the battery from the circuit. Then you hand crank the engine into action, rev it up to speed, then snap on a light which is coupled to the system: The light would probably blow out like a flash bulb because one small lamp is not enough generator load. Most engine-driven generators are wound such that open-circuit or no-load voltage is very high unless reduced by load or by external voltage control circuits. Without load or control a 12-volt generator might snap out as much as 100 volts, a light load may reduce it to 22 volts, but it requires a respectable load to drag the voltage down to an acceptable level (Fig. 36). Loaded by a partly charged battery, a nominal 12-volt system will operate while charging at about 13 volts. With fully charged battery and the generator operating, the voltage will be about 14 volts. On the other hand, when the starter is straining to crank a cold engine, the voltage will drop to 8 or 9 volts; so it is obvious that a perfectly normal battery will operate at different voltages to match conditions. A 12-volt battery, fully charged but quiescent, will indicate 12.6 volts. However, battery voltage alone is not an accurate indicator of cell condition. In order to make voltage readings useful, current must be measured at the same time to indicate whether the battery is being charged or discharged.

Most newer marine engines incorporate a generator with an external voltage control box (Fig. 37). These generators usually have two commutator brushes rather than three, and the unit is series wound with one end of the field winding being "open." If this "open" end is externally grounded, the generator will operate at maximum charge; if the end is grounded through a resistor, the generator will operate at reduced charge. That is how

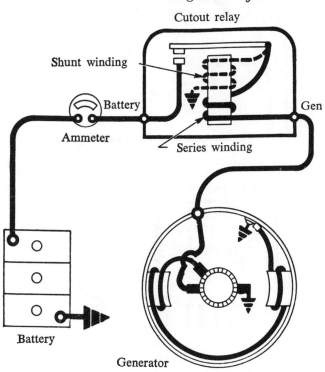

Fig. 36. A *schematic diagram of a "third brush" type of generator charging circuit.*

the control box works; it varies the resistance of the generator field winding in response to voltage changes in the charging circuit. As the battery becomes charged, circuit voltage rises and the control responds by increasing generator field circuit resistance.

The battery may be completely removed from the circuit which has an externally controlled generator and the voltage will not run wild as with an older system. However, the control box is designed to operate in conjunction

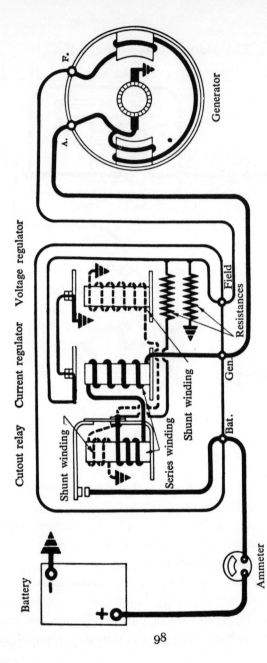

Fig 37. A schematic diagram of a generator charging circuit incorporating external voltage and current control.

98

with a battery, and prolonged operation without a battery may ruin the control. Many boats have a master switch in the battery circuit arranged so that when the switch is open the batteries are completely removed from operation. After the boat's engine is started it is possible to open this switch and to operate the ignition and other accessories directly from the generator, but it is a poor practice because it throws a terrible strain on the voltage control machinery.

It is interesting to think of the boat's battery as a big water tank. When electricity is required by an accessory or electronic device, juice flows from the tank to the device. If the current demand is heavy, the tank empties in tubsfull. An engine starter, for example, draws by the barrel; a tiny light draws by a thimble. The generator pumps back into the tank at a moderate rate, and if the system is balanced, the generator just matches the loads, the tank acting as a source of surge capacity.

It is easy to see what happens if we put demands on the tank and do not replenish the supply. It dries up. The battery dies.

But suppose the generator keeps pumping into the tank and there is no drain. Can the electricity overflow?

Electrons cannot overflow the battery, but electricity is a form of energy and can convert to other forms and then spill over. That is what happens in your boat's battery if you charge it full then keep the generator charging more. The current which the generator forces into an already charged battery is converted into heat, then dissipated. That does not sound too drastic (just wasting a little heat) and if the amount of current is modest, the heat is trifling and no harm done. The battery is simply warmed a little. But if a heavy charging current is forced into a full battery, the heat becomes intense and will ruin the cells.

Of course the analogy comparing battery and water tank is a little misleading. The battery stores no electricity; charging current is converted to chemical energy within the cells. When the battery is coupled to a circuit the chemical energy is reconverted to electricity.

The trick is done like this: A 12-volt storage battery consists of six 2-volt cells connected in series and mounted in a common case. Each cell contains two groups of plates. The negative group is of sponge lead; the positive group is lead-peroxide and the sets of plates are electrically insulated from each other by separators and immersed in electrolyte. The electrolyte is a mixture of sulphuric acid and water, the percentage of acid being about 39.2 when cells are fully charged. The percentage of acid varies with the charge of the battery, and inasmuch as the acid is extremely heavy, the weight or specific gravity of the electrolyte varies greatly with state-of-charge of each cell. The specific gravity of the electrolyte in a fully charged cell is 1.300 at 60 degrees F. (Water is 1.00.) When the battery is discharged the acid is used up (combined with elements of the plates) and the gravity falls to about 1.140 when the cells are finally dead. During recharging, the acid which was used up is regenerated by electro-chemical action of the charging current upon the plates, and it reappears in the electrolyte, thereby increasing the gravity of the mixture.

It is apparent, then, that the weight or gravity of the electrolyte is a direct measure of state-of-charge of the battery. Measure the electrolyte's weight, and you measure the amount of charge. Weighing the electrolyte is easy: Simply suck a little of the fluid into a hydrometer and read the scale on the float. The higher the float, the heavier the fluid, and consequently the more powerful

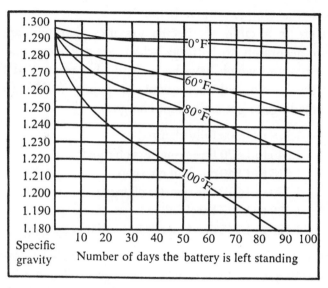

Fig. 38. *Battery self-discharge rates at various temperatures. Note that at elevated temperatures the battery discharges itself quickly.*

the charge. However, some temperature correction must be applied if the most accurate hydrometer indication is desired. Most hydrometers are designed to give correct reading either at 60 or 80 degrees F. Find out which temperature your hydrometer is calibrated for, then apply the necessary correction. Here is the correction procedure suggested by Delco Remy, makers of the well known Delco battery:

"For gravities above 1.220 a correction of 4 points (0.004) should be made for each deviation of 10 degrees F. This correction should be added when the temperature is above the hydrometer calibration point, and subtracted when the temperature is below."

Here is a table of specific gravities that will apply quite accurately to batteries which are not more than a year old and which have been reasonably treated. If the battery is old, subtract about 25 points (.025) from the readings to get equivalent charge:

> 1.275 to 1.300 fully charged
> 1.245 to 1.270 three quarters charged
> 1.215 to 1.240 one half charged
> 1.180 to 1.210 one quarter charged
> 1.150 to 1.175 barely alive
> 1.120 to 1.145 dead, needs immediate charging

A battery need not be in service or be loaded in order to discharge; the battery will discharge itself like a leaky water tank. Ambient temperature has a marked effect upon the self-discharge rate of a cell (Fig. 38). A battery stored at 70 degrees F. will lose about one point of electrolyte gravity per day. The same battery stored at 100 degrees F. will lose three points per day. There is negligible loss at zero degrees F., and the self-discharge is faster in old batteries than in new ones.

Occasionally a battery will be neglected for many months with the result that it loses all traces of charge. Such a maltreated battery can sometimes be restored to useful service provided, however, that the cells have not dried out too much and the plates are not excessively sulphated. To rejuvenate a totally run-down battery, fill the cells with water to the correct level, then place the battery on 3 or 4 ampere charge. Leave the battery on charge at this easy rate for several days. If after at least 60 hours of slow charge the battery has not revived, write it off as a total loss.

One warning about recharging completely exhausted batteries: Do not put them on constant potential "fast charges." These machines are designed to charge at a terrific rate, as much as 60 or 100 amperes when coupled to a healthy battery. The rate of constant potential charge diminishes as the battery counter-voltage rises, but obviously the dead battery is close to zero and therefore the charger will work all-out trying to pump up the sickly cells. Such a high rate of charge is harmful to a battery that has lain fallow for months.

Battery manufacturers do not condemn the use of fast chargers for new, healthy batteries. In fact the use of fast chargers is strongly recommended for the initial charging of "dry-charged batteries" after the electrolyte is poured in. Fast charging has a bad name with some battery users because they have seen the results of uncontrolled fast charging. A discharged battery will safely accept charge rates of from 40 to 60 amperes provided that the cells are not allowed to overheat. Heat can buckle the plates and ruin a battery, therefore the key to safe fast-charging is accurate control of generated heat. Some chargers limit heat by the use of an automatic timer, set to cut the charge before excess heating occurs. Other chargers taper the cur-

rent in response to increasing battery voltage, and a third
type of charger is controlled by a thermostatically trig-
gered switch actually immersed in the warming electrolyte (Fig. 39).

Selecting the correct battery for your boat is a fairly
easy job, and by a little intelligent estimating you should

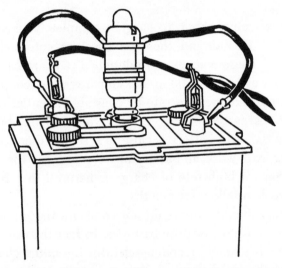

Fig. 39. *A special thermostat immersed in the battery electrolyte to guard against high temperatures during fast charging.*

pick the right battery, keeping in mind that a battery too
large is better than one too small. Consider the amount of
electrical equipment on your boat and the length of time
the equipment must operate without the generator to
lend a hand. Consider, also, the number of engine starts.
Above all, keep in mind that no matter how big the battery, it will fail in service if generator capacity is too small

to match the drain. A given size generator can push out only so much current without frying; so if your engine's generator is too puny, install one of higher capacity. Most marine engine manufacturers can supply oversize, heavy-duty generators for their engines.

In making battery selection, consider the twenty-hour rate. This is a measure of battery electrical capacity. For example; if a battery has plate size and electrolyte volume which enable it to deliver 5 amperes for 20 hours, it has 5 times 20, or 100 ampere hours capacity. This is a convenient yardstick for comparing batteries and is an aid to estimating the size required for your boat.

Supposing that you want to pick a set of 12 volt batteries which will enable you to anchor for the night independent of charging; what capacity batteries will be needed to operate the following:

1. A radio	2 amperes for 4 hours	8 ampere hours
2. A reading light	5 amperes for 6 hours	30 ampere hours
3. An anchor light	1 ampere for 9 hours	9 ampere hours
4. A bilge pump	10 amperes for 1/10 hour	1 ampere hour
5. A refrigerator (40% duty cycle)	30 amperes for 4 hours	120 ampere hours
	Total:	168 ampere hours.

Assuming that the accessory batteries are not required to start the engines, this installation should be provided with batteries totaling 200 ampere hours capacity, and even then, unless the batteries are at top charge, the refrigerator is going to be struggling by morning. A more conservative practice would be to provide 300 ampere hours capacity, and if the same batteries are used for engine starting, 400 ampere hours.

The best practice is to provide each engine with its own

individual battery for starting and ignition, then operate the accessories from a separate bank of batteries. Then if the lights, radio, refrigerator and bilge pump deplete their own batteries, the engine will still start in the morning.

If your boat is diesel equipped, it is wise to select a battery especially designed for diesel starting service. These batteries have high current output, rugged plates and special terminal binding posts to transmit the terrific current necessary to the diesel starter.

Whether your boat is gasoline or diesel, you show good judgment when you select a battery more than large enough to see you through the tough spots, i.e., hard starts with damp engine, periods when the generator is dead and unexpected extra loads in emergency situations.

Battery life can be considerably extended simply by installing the unit correctly and by assuring that the charging circuit is well adjusted. Two great battery enemies are heavy vibration and overcharging. Both can be prevented.

The battery should be securely mounted in a suitable box or rugged platform and should be clamped or strapped firmly so that vibration does not cause it to walk around. If the boat vibrates appreciably, place the battery in a box which is form fitting and lined with thick pads of sponge rubber. Be sure the box has a drain in case acid should spill, and be sure the battery is adequately ventilated. The sponge rubber lined box will increase the battery's life because the rubber will absorb vibration which would otherwise deteriorate battery plates.

The best protection against overcharging and overheating is automatic voltage control. Many modern marine engines are supplied with external generator control, and if you have such a motor you have no need to worry about overcharging, provided, of course, that the control box is operating according to Hoyle. If the voltage control is functioning properly the charge rate will taper down to just a few amperes when the cells are completely charged.

Overcharge protection with third brush type generator not fitted with external control is more difficult. All you can do is to adjust the generator charge rate at a level that will avoid serious overcharge, and be especially sure that the cells are kept topped-up with water. Plenty of water helps prevent overcharge damage.

Is it necessary to use distilled water in a storage battery? The battery companies recommend distilled or especially treated water, but they state that it is also permissible to use ordinary tap water if reasonably mineral free and soft. Water which has passed through a household water softener is not recommended, but any water at all is better than none; even hard water is better for the battery than dry plates.

If you want the battery to spin the starter with zest, you must provide fat, husky battery cables. A starter motor draws hundreds of amperes while cranking the engine. A good battery is capable of supplying these many amperes, but requires a fat pipe line to transmit the buckets full of current to the starter. The longer the cables, the fatter they must be in order to handle the load without undue resistance. When in doubt, use heavier cables, or double up on them; they just cannot be too husky.

Here is a quick test to ascertain whether your starter cables are heavy enough (Fig. 40):

Use a voltmeter with full scale reading of only a few volts. Secure one meter test prod to the battery binding post which is attached to the ungrounded cable (the one to the starter switch). Secure the other prod to the starter

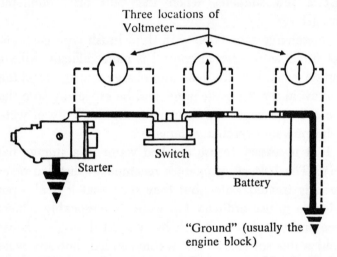

Fig. 40. *Using a voltmeter to test the starter cables for resistance. With starter grinding away, the meter should read less than 0.3 volts.*

switch binding post. (You are simply paralleling the cable with the voltmeter.) Watch the voltmeter and press the starter button. The voltmeter should read no more than 0.3 volts; higher reading indicates excess drop across the cable and the cable should be made heavier or shorter or both. The exact same test may be repeated on the cable leading from switch to starter motor and on the ground cable.

Another useful test may be made with the voltmeter to determine if the battery has good reserve capacity for engine starting. For this test the cells should be fully charged and the engine cold with ignition off. Place the voltmeter test leads directly on the battery terminals; the instrument should read about 12.6 volts (for a nominal 6 volt system it should read 6.3). Now, depress the starter switch. If the battery has good reserve capabilities the voltmeter will read 9.7 volts or higher (4.8 volts for 6 volt system).

If your boat is out of service during the cold winter months, remove the battery and store it in a cool, dry place, such as your cellar. Keep the cells fully charged to prevent sulphation. If the battery is stored out-of-doors, remember that it can freeze and be destroyed unless well charged. Here are the temperatures at which the battery will freeze:

Specific Gravity of Electrolyte	Freezing Point (Degrees F.)
1.280	minus 90
1.250	minus 62
1.200	minus 16
1.150	plus 5
1.100	plus 19

Check on two things when you re-install the battery in the spring: be sure the cells are fully charged, and remove all traces of corrosion and oxidation from terminals. Even a faint layer of oxide on the binding posts can cause a high resistance connection or even an open circuit—troubles which are hard to locate. The best way to clean

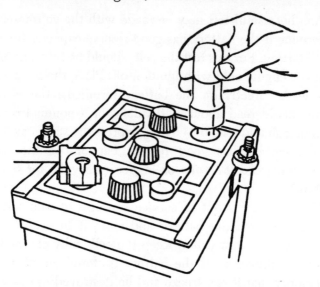

Fig. 41. *Using a special steel brush to clean the battery posts.*

cable clamps and binding posts is with a small, stiff metal brush (Fig. 41). Use the brush and burnish the surfaces until they shine, then couple them up tightly and you will benefit from an excellent connection.

Chapter Seven

SPARK PLUGS FOR MARINE ENGINES

SPARK PLUGS are the pampered pets of the ignition system. All other components work diligently for the sole purpose of supplying the plugs with hot, properly timed voltage; but if the plugs falter, all the juice is wasted. Spark plugs are starkly simple, yet their pinpoints of miniature lightning trigger the engine's brawny power.

It is important to equip your engine with the correct plugs and to maintain the plugs in perfect condition, because no matter how well the balance of the engine is timed, tuned and tended, if the humble plugs are sooty, foul, cracked or burned, the motor will be sick.

Poor spark plugs waste gasoline, cause power loss, foul the cylinders and cause rough running. They can even damage structural parts of the engine.

Marine engines are sometimes sent to the shop for complete tear down and overhaul when all that is really required is a fresh set of spark plugs, properly installed and gapped. And outside the shop there are many boats operating this very minute with blowsy spark plugs, plugs which eat gasoline, cause tough starting, and make the engine wheezy and cantankerous.

How do plugs differ? How are they constructed? How can they ruin an engine's pep?

The simplest way to learn about plug construction is to

take an old junk plug and wallop it with a hammer: The porcelain will shatter and show that the component is made of three principal parts: The long porcelain insulator, the center conductor or "hot" electrode, and the steel shell which incorporates the hexagonal section for socket wrench grip. Resistor type spark plugs have a small spring and a little carbon cylinder inside the porcelain insulator; that is all there is to a spark plug—simple component.

But not all spark plugs are identical. The first difference is in the threads which have various diameters and lengths, dimensions which must exactly match the threads tapped into the engine casting. Motor manufacturers specify which model plugs fit their engines, and plug makers have conversion charts showing interchangeability between brand names. American marine engines have used thread sizes ⅞ inch, ½ inch, 18 mm, 14 mm, and 10 mm. Currently the most popular thread size is 14 mm.

Plug threads have various lengths. A plug with long threaded section, designed for a thick cylinder head is described as having a long reach. A plug with short threads and stubby lower body has a short reach. If a short reach plug is used in an engine designed for a long one, ignition may be erratic; in fact, may quit altogether in some circumstances. If long reach plug is used where short reach is indicated, the engine may suffer from pre-ignition, and in some cases the plug will damage the engine.

A skipper need not specify thread size or reach when buying spark plugs, all he need do is specify the plug part number, such as Champion XJ-8, Auto-Lite AR-51 or

AC-74. The plug designation covers all characteristics, both physical and electrical. Plugs which have identical electrical characteristics, but different threads, have different numbers.

The heat range or thermal characteristics of a spark plug are important and are altogether responsible for the performance of a correctly fitted plug. A plug's heat range determines its ability to serve a particular engine.

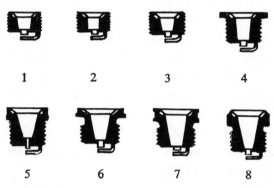

Fig. 42. *The higher the number, the hotter the heat range of the spark plug. Plug No. 1 is the coolest; plug No. 8 is the hottest.*

The all important heat number (relative operating temperature of the plug) is determined by the internal length of the center porcelain insulator which carries the center electrode from outside down to the spark gap. The longer this insulator, the hotter the plug. It is the length within the combustion space which counts, not the visible length sticking out of the engine head. A long, lanky insulator exposed to searing hot gases will become incandescent; a stubby one will be cool. Temperature is determined by the length of heat path inside the plug. Fig. 42 shows the phenomenon clearly.

The center ceramic insulator is the part which varies most in temperature and is most sensitive to combustion heat. The center shape determines whether a plug is hot or cold. The steel shell and grounded electrode are in close thermal contact with engine casting and can shed heat quickly, so rapidly, in fact, that these metal parts operate at a temperature close to that of engine head and block. Not so the center electrode. The porcelain surface is exposed to combustion heat, and high temperatures must travel the porcelain length before being grounded and dissipated through the engine casting and cooling water. The longer the electrode, the hotter the tip. Hot plugs with long center ceramic usually have higher serial numbers than cooler plugs. Thus an AC plug No. M-41 is cooler than No. M-48, and an Auto-Lite A-3 is cooler than an A-11 (Fig. 43).

Each engine requires spark plugs of certain heat range, the range requirement being determined by the motor manufacturer before the engine reaches the market. The factory recommended plug should be used unless unusual service conditions warrant a change.

Low compression engines use relatively hot plugs, while high compression, high speed engines tend toward cooler plugs. Cool plugs are used in high compression engines because of the elevated mean temperature in cylinder and combustion chamber. A hot plug used in a high compression cylinder will cause pre-ignition, detonation and heavy knocking due to the ceramic operating at red heat. Excess plug temperature will ignite the compressed mixture before spark, consequently the engine will operate as though incorrectly timed. On the other hand, if an engine is fitted with plugs too cold, the results are almost as bad: An excessively cool plug is unable to burn carbon and soot from the center insulator; as a result the plug becomes foul and is soon electrically short circuited. Then the engine quits.

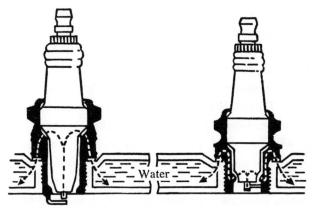

Fig. 43. *The long insulator of the plug at the left will cause it to run hotter than the plug at the right.*

Plug selection, then, is a nice balance between plug so hot that it pre-ignites, and plug so cool that it soots up. As in most engineering matters, correct selection is an intelligent balance between extremes.

Sometimes unusual service conditions will warrant changing from the recommended plug to one of different heat range. For example, if an engine is run extensively near idle the plugs may tend to foul and cause roughness. In this case it may be wise to switch to plugs one or two heat numbers hotter to eliminate fouling. For such service as all day trolling, the hotter plugs may be just the ticket, but for extended advanced throttle operation the torrid plugs may cause trouble. The compromise might be to use the hot plugs on days when lots of trolling is planned, then switch to cooler plugs for long, hard runs.

Outboard motors are tough on plugs because of oil mixed in the gasoline. The diluted oil does not burn as readily as gasoline and the partly burned products of combustion help foul the plugs. As with inboard engines, fouling due to trolling may be reduced with hotter plugs. In addition, fouling is reduced somewhat by using specially compounded outboard motor lubricating oil in the gasoline. This stable oil is brewed to give excellent lubrication to outboard motor innards, then to burn cleanly along with the fuel after lubrication is completed. Inasmuch as an outboard motor consumes more than 250 times as much oil as an inboard, it is obvious that oil characteristics have an important bearing on spark plug life.

Every boat should carry several spare spark plugs, and this is particularly true for outboard boats which should carry a complete set of spares. Extra plugs should be aboard because if a plug is broken or badly sooted, it is impossible to repair afloat. If outboard plugs become oiled or carbon coated the engine may be impossible to re-start unless fresh, clean, properly gapped plugs are substituted for the soiled ones. Keep spares wrapped carefully in oiled paper or a tight jar or otherwise packed so they stay bone dry, clean and ready to go when needed (Fig. 44). Rusty, moldy plugs are not of much use in an emergency.

How often should plugs be changed? That depends

upon severity of use. There is no flexible rule, though perhaps 250 to 300 hours is a good round figure for inboards and half those hours for outboards. Inspect the plugs. If they are burned and charred, if the porcelain is cracked

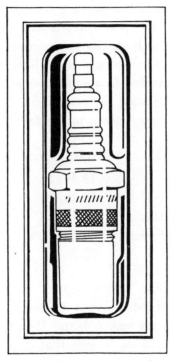

Fig. 44. *This waterproof marine spark plug pack keeps spare plugs dry and rust free.*

or chipped, or the electrodes are pitted away, change them. New plugs cost little.

Be careful about two things when changing plugs: Inhale a good lungful of sea air and blow away all dirt and grit from the plug recess before removing the old plug. Use correct torque when tightening down the new one. If you save your breath and leave dirt in the recess, a slug of grit will fall into the cylinder when the plug comes out. Prevent this because the dirt will help grind away valuable metal. Correct tightening torque is the middle ground between stripping threads and having gas leaks. Most engine manuals specify torque, small plugs needing less than large, and aluminum heads having less than iron. A few dollars invested in a good torque wrench are well spent. If correct torque for your particular engine is unknown, use the figure given in the following tabulation:

Plug Thread	Cast Iron Head	Aluminum Head
10 mm.	12 lb. ft.	10 lb. ft.
14 mm.	25 lb. ft.	22 lb. ft.
18 mm. Tapered Seat	17 lb. ft.	Not Used
18 mm. Regular Seat	30 lb. ft.	25 lb. ft.
7/8 inch	35 lb. ft.	30 lb. ft.

Remember, these torque figures are maximum and should not be exceeded. When in doubt, use less torque because a slight gas leak is better than stripped threads in engine casting. Also, be sure that threads on the plug and engine casting are immaculately clean and that each new plug is fitted with a fresh, springy gasket.

Proper tightening torque has a serious bearing on correct plug temperature. Most of a plug's heat is conveyed through the seating washer to the engine casting. Insufficient tightening of the plug reduces heat path efficiency and can cause the plug to overheat.

It is easy to crack or break the ceramic body when installing a new plug. If the wrench slips from the hex shell it usually strikes the porcelain a sharp blow and finishes off the plug. Prevent such grief (and eliminate skinned knuckles) by using a deep socket wrench made for the specific purpose of reaching over the plug insulator and fitting the hexagonal shell correctly. There is one spark plug wrench on the market which has the upper part of its box socket lined with rubber to protect brittle porcelain during the tightening operation.

Fig. 45. *A handy pocket tool having round wire feeler gauges and gap setting slot for adjusting spark plugs.*

Marine spark plugs are subjected to lots of dampness and sometimes to salty mist, both of which reduce the surface insulation resistance of the plug insulator. Sometimes the resistance is lowered so much that spark snaps across the outside of the plug instead of across the gap inside; then the engine misses or quits. Eliminate this trouble by keeping the outside of the plugs dry and shiny. Buff them with a dry cloth and a little carbon tet, or better still, buff them and apply a thin coat of silicone compound to the entire external surface of the plugs, metal included. Silicone compounds designed for application to ignition components may be bought at stores that sell automotive or marine engine parts and accessories.

The distance between electrodes is called the gap and is adjustable by slight bending of the side or ground electrode. Engines have individual gap requirements which vary anywhere from 0.025 inch to 0.035 inch depending upon the design of combustion chamber and ig-

Set Gap.

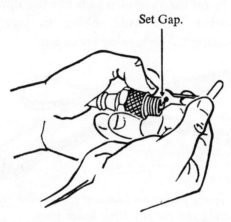

Fig. 46. *Carefully setting the gap by moving the side electrode.*

nition system. Use a round wire feeler gauge and measure the gap when installing new plugs or servicing old ones (Fig. 45). If the gap requires adjustment, carefully bend the side electrode until desired spacing is had. Do not try to bend the center electrode; the force will break the ceramic insulator (Fig. 46).

Exactly what gap does your engine require? Look in the engine manual. If no manual is available and you have to guess, try 0.025 inch. Generally, it is better to have the gap a trifle undersize rather than too large. Also, the gap will increase as the electrodes burn.

In trouble-shooting and tune-up, keep in mind that too small a gap may cause poor idling and power loss at a high speed and may also invite a dead cylinder due to carbon whiskers bridging the gap between electrodes. Excess gap, on the other hand, usually causes hard starting and may contribute to missing at open throttle. In addition, overly large plug gaps raise the voltage in the balance of the ignition system and stress the components, inviting breakdown.

What about resistor spark plugs?

Resistor plugs have a carbon resistor built into the ceramic insulator, the resistor being part of the electrical conductor between center electrode and wire terminal (Fig. 47). The resistor is generally about 10,000 ohms and its purpose is to dampen radio frequency oscillation which takes place in the high voltage circuit after ionization at the plug gap. The resistor also allows slightly larger plug gap without damage to the ignition coil. The chief beauty of the resistor plugs is that they suppress radio ignition noise. They do not reduce engine power.

Some marine engines are fitted with shielded type spark plugs and shielded high voltage wiring as a means of eliminating radio interference (Fig. 48). The use of shielded plugs eliminates the need for resistor plugs. However, the best shielding of high voltage ignition wires may not eliminate interference from radio frequency ignition noise picked up by the battery voltage wires and re-radiated all over the boat. Remember, too, that shield plugs alone are helpless in reducing static unless used in conjunction with shielded wires, correct fittings, plus shielded distributor and coil.

Remember that spark plugs are important, but so are

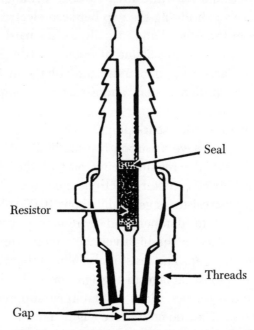

Fig. 47. *Cross section of an AC resistor spark plug.*

the other ignition system components. The plugs can do a good job only if supplied with hot, properly timed voltage. If the plugs seem to give trouble in spite of best selection and servicing, give attention to the balance of ignition components and wiring. If plugs soot up, get oily and foul regardless of heat number and with good spark, the cause

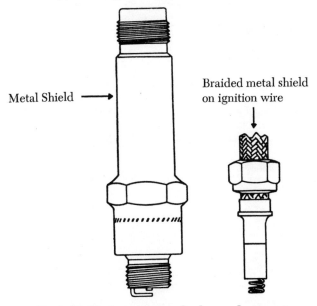

Metal Shield

Braided metal shield
on ignition wire

Fig. 48. *A shielded marine spark plug and connector.*

may be worn cylinders, sloppy valves or broken piston
ring. There are some troubles that even the best plugs cannot cure.

Chapter Eight

THE MARINE ENGINE
STARTING SYSTEM

THE MARINE ENGINE starting system is an essential accessory to any power plant. Starting systems range in complexity all the way from the simple hand crank to complex, remotely controlled pneumatic/hydraulic circuits. Regardless of complexity, however, it is essential that the starter be trustworthy because a marine engine is only as reliable as the system which fires it into action.

What good is a super-duper, 300 horsepower, high-compression, supercharged V-8 engine with 12-volt electric starter and a dead battery? It is useless.

Only last September a sick starter caused an emergency situation replete with such window dressing as inverted flag, flares, underwear waved on the end of an oar and loud yells for help.

It seems that the skipper of a forty-footer put out of Bodkin Creek and proceeded to the widest point of the Chesapeake where he anchored for a day of fishing and relaxation with friends. They passed the long, pleasant, summer day playing the radio, making calls on the transmitter, fooling with the fathometer, and chilling beer in the electric refrigerator.

When evening came, the weather turned sour, the wind

blew up from the southeast and a drizzle started, so the skipper decided to head home. Confidently, he flipped the ignition switch of the powerful engine and nonchalantly hit the starter button. Alas, instead of a throaty roar, the engine gave but a bilious grunt and refused further activity.

Obviously the battery was dead; the drain of using electrical gear all day and the lack of charging had exhausted the cells. Now what good was that big, powerful engine nestled under the deck?

The weather was now really foul and the bay mighty rough; the nautical guests were nervous and uncomfortable and the next hour was spent in frantic signaling for help, and other activities which bordered on panic. Finally help arrived and the fine, powerful, shining white yacht was towed ignominiously home.

The whole fracas was caused by the engine's starting system and its failure to function. The malfunction was brought on by the skipper who neglected the cardinal rule of planning ahead. He exhausted the starting batteries through prolonged use and forgot to conserve enough charge to restart the engine after a day of carefree fun.

In the instance cited above, the engine was started by an electric starter and the starter energized by the same bank of batteries used to vitalize a boatload of accessories such as radio, transmitter, lights, refrigerator and a pressurized water system. True, the skipper was much at fault for running down the batteries, but the battery arrangement was also a contributor to the panic situation.

In a correct installation, one set of batteries is used to run all the accessories, and a separate battery is provided for engine starting only. This engine starting battery has no connection to the others, and is connected only to the starter motor and engine ignition. Then, even though the accessory batteries are drained to complete exhaustion, the engine will restart and the boat will go home proudly under her own steam. While running home, the generator will pick up the load and supply current for necessary accessories, such as running lights.

An auxiliary generator driven by a small, hand-started gasoline engine would have saved the day for the skipper who backed himself into the dead battery situation. A small, engine-driven auxiliary generator can be started by hand crank or rope starter and will recharge the batteries independent of the propulsion machinery. Such an auxiliary charging system is almost a "must" on a yacht used intermittently and sporting considerable electric and electronic gear.

The house cat electric starter is by far the most popular starter used on gasoline or diesel marine engines, but there are other types of starters in current use, some of which are becoming more popular, particularly on diesels. Starting systems which do not depend upon battery power are the gasoline or donkey engine starter, used extensively by Caterpillar, the hydro/pneumatic starter, compressed air starter, inertia starter, shotgun starter, and, of course, the dear old reliable hand crank and rope starter.

A typical hydro/pneumatic starting system is the General Motors Hydrostarter which is designed to replace electric starters on diesel engines and which can be supplied as optional equipment on the well known General Motors marine diesels (Fig. 49).

The essential parts of the General Motors Hydrostarter

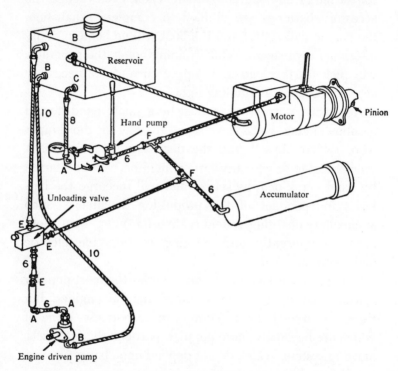

Fig. 49. *Diagram of complete Hydrotor starting system.*

are an oil reservoir, engine-driven pump, hand pump, accumulator and starter motor unit. It works as follows: While the diesel is operating it drives a small, high-pressure hydraulic pump; the pump forces oil from the reservoir into an accumulator against terrific pressure. The accumulator is a thick-walled cylinder containing a floating piston and a charge of nitrogen gas which is under 1,250 pounds per square inch pressure in the "discharged" state, and 3,250 per square inch when "charged." In other words, the nitrogen gas acts as a powerful spring to energize the system. The engine-driven pump forces oil into the accumulator until the pressure is full-up; then an automatic relief valve checks the flow. The starter motor is a seven-piston hydraulic swashplate motor, incorporating engaging mechanism, overrunning clutch and pinion for flywheel drive (Fig. 50).

The Hydrostarter has a control valve in place of the conventional starter switch, and when a start is desired, the valve is opened to allow high pressure oil to flow from the accumulator to starter motor. The starter spins about 1,500 rpm. and whirls the diesel into action. Naturally, use of the starter decreases nitrogen pressure, but this is restored in a few minutes by the engine-driven pump (Fig. 51).

One attractive feature of the Hydrostarter is the hand pump provided to restore pressure should the accumulator be depleted through numerous unsuccessful start attempts. Ten or fifteen minutes of healthful exercise will recharge the accumulator, and such exercise is far more fruitful than yelling to the lonesome winds for help when a battery goes dead.

The Hydrostarter has the advantage of being manually rechargeable; it also completely eliminates the hazardous electrical system from diesel boats in cases where this is desirable. Electric starters require extreme current, amperage which poses a fire hazard in the event of loose connections, short circuit, inadequate switches or under-

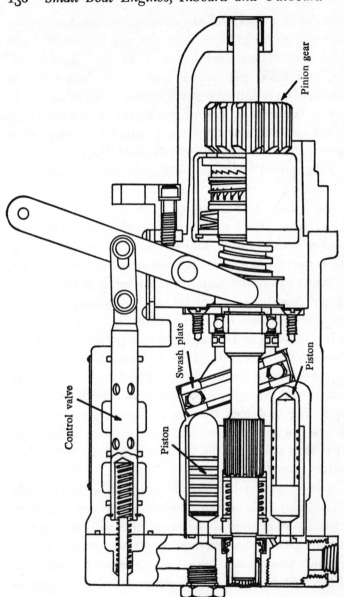

Fig. 50. Cutaway view of a hydraulic starter motor unit.

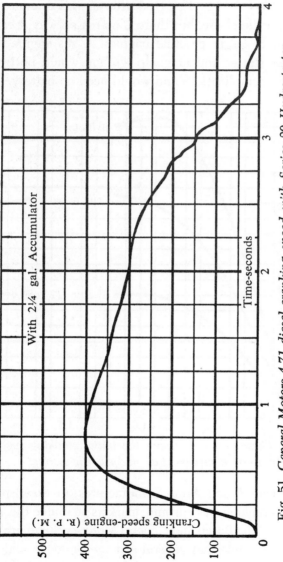

Fig. 51. *General Motors 4-71 diesel cranking speed with Series 20 Hydrostarter.*

sized battery cables. The Hydrostarter was designed primarily for diesel use, but there is no reason why it cannot be fitted to larger gasoline engines. A gas engine fitted with this starter and magneto ignition would be free of electrical complications and would need no battery.

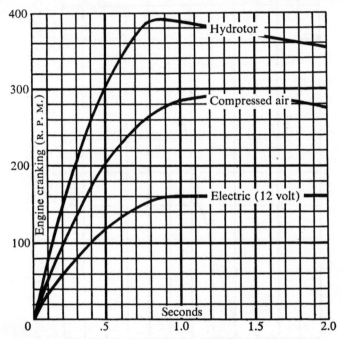

Fig. 52. *These curves compare the initial cranking speeds of Bosch Hydrotor, compressed air and electric starter.*

American Bosch Arma manufactures an excellent hydraulic cranking system and markets it under the name Hydrotor. The Bosch and General Motors systems are identical in principle and general arrangement, the main difference being in constructional details of the components.

Pressure is recharged in the Bosch system by engine-driven, hand or electric pump. In boats having large battery capacity, the electric-driven pump may replace the engine-driven one as the prime source of energy to recharge the accumulator (Fig. 52).

The following table gives data on two popular sizes of Bosch Hydrotor:

Cranking Motor	Model No. CMA	Model No. CMB
For engines with piston displacement up to:	500 cu. in. diesel 1,200 cu. in. gasoline	1,100 cu. in. diesel 2,500 cu. in. gasoline
Operating pressure:	1,000—3,000 psi.	1,500—3,000 psi.
Speed range:	0—7,500 r.p.m.	0—7,000 r.p.m.
Lock torque @ 1,000 psi.	17 lb. ft.	
@ 1,500 psi.	25 lb. ft.	40 lb. ft.
@ 3,000 psi.	50 lb. ft.	80 lb. ft.
Motor weight:	16 pounds	21 pounds

The gasoline donkey engine starter for diesel engines is usually thought of as being applied to large engines only. However, Caterpillar will supply this reliable and successful starting system on engines as small as 250 cubic inches (Fig. 53). For sheer, dogged cranking power under all conditions, the gasoline starter is king. The starter usually consists of a small, two-cylinder, four-cycle gasoline engine with rope or hand crank starter. (Some large ones have an electric starter.) The procedure for firing-up the diesel is to first start the little gasoline donkey engine, then engage a hand clutch and make the little gasoline engine rotate the diesel until the big engine fires and runs on its own.

One beauty of the system is that the two engines have a common cooling system, therefore, in cold weather the little starter engine warms the water and manifolds of

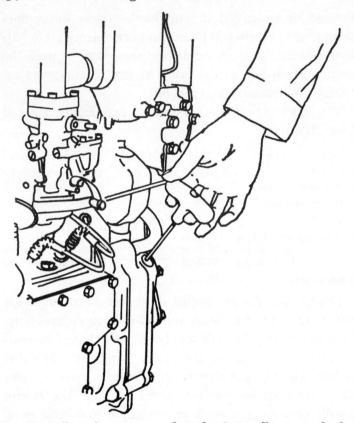

Fig. 53. *Pulling the starter cord on the Caterpillar two-cylinder gasoline starter motor.*

the big engine. It is a built-in cold weather starting aid. Length of cranking time is almost unlimited. In fact, one old salt we know has a pleasant cold weather routine: He fires up the starting motor and lets it crank the diesel with compression release while he cooks himself a cup of hot coffee in the galley. When coffee is ready, he knows the big diesel is ready too, so he ambles up to the engine, throws on the compression and the pre-warmed diesel fires at once.

For marine application, the only drawback to the donkey engine starter is the gasoline engine fire hazard. Diesel boats are blessed with a reduced fire hazard because of their fuel's low flash point and lack of volatility. It is unfortunate that the donkey engine brings several gallons of gasoline aboard. Perhaps some day they will have a tiny hand-started diesel donkey engine to start the big diesel!

Compressed air starting is used on a few marine diesels of modest size, but it is not a popular system. The diesel is fitted with a small air-operated motor, an engine-driven compressor, a hand-operated compressor and air storage tanks. Air is compressed into the storage tanks by the engine-driven compressor. When starting is required, a valve is opened and the compressed air runs from the tanks to the starter motor which spins the diesel into action. As with the Hydrostarter, a hand pump is provided for emergency recharging.

The shotgun starter is a most spectacular performer and more fun to use than a barrel of monkeys. It is probably fortunate that few American engines are equipped with this fiendish device, because when the engine is cranked the starter booms with a roar exceeding a cannon's violence. If an engine refuses to start after being twisted by one of these bombs, the engine is indeed sick.

The shotgun starter gets its energy from an oversize shotgun shell loaded with a healthy charge of smokeless gunpowder. The starter motor contains a piston mounted on the end of a helical shaft in such a manner that as the piston is pushed down, the shaft rotates. The end of the shaft is dog-clutched to the engine's crankshaft, consequently as the piston moves down, the engine rotates. The space above the piston is connected by high pressure steel tubing to the breech mechanism where the king-size shotgun shell is fired. The engine is cranked by firing the shell; combustion of gunpowder creates violent pressure which pushes the piston down and spins the engine with terrific torque. It is as though a giant grabbed the end of the crankshaft and spun it like a child's top.

The real fun comes when the shotgun starter piston reaches bottom. At this juncture an exhaust valve pops open and releases the pent up gases with the most nerve shattering bang imaginable. When another start is required, the operator generally needs a little dollop of rum as a nerve steadier.

Starters using the shotgun technique are found only on a few marine engines, usually war surplus machines. They have the beauty of cranking at terrific speed; their disadvantages are the startling noise and the necessity of stocking the special shells; a new shell for each start.

A few large gasoline marine engines use the inertia starter, a type much used on aircraft. The inertia starter is basically a small, steel flywheel with gearing and clutch device so that it can be coupled to the engine. By means of step-up gearing, the little flywheel is accelerated to 15,000 rpm. or more; when fully accelerated it is clutched through reduction gearing to the engine crankshaft and its stored energy rotates the engine. Power for accelerating the wheel may be supplied by electric motor or by hand crank.

Inertia starters offer the advantage that large engines may be started with modest size batteries or may be cranked by hand in emergency. Their drawbacks are that cranking speed is not high, and they only rotate the engine a few revolutions for each acceleration of the fly-wheel.

No discussion of engine starters would be complete without mention of the venerable hand crank. Why is this trusty old device in such disrepute? We do not suggest that it be brought back as the prime means of starting marine engines, but why discard it completely as an emergency means of starting? The humble hand crank would have bailed out that proud, stranded yachtsman helpess in the middle of Chesapeake Bay. You can push a modern car and get it started with pooped-out battery, but you cannot get out and push your boat. Then why not have a crank available for emergency?

We have heard it said that most of the new engines are too big for hand cranking. Well, this may be true for one man on the crank, but how about a crank for two, or even three people? It sounds funny, but it is practical. During the war we used to hand crank the big 670 cubic inch engines on the M-3 light tank. Nobody liked it, but it worked in a pinch. We used a crank with long handle and nice smooth bearings. Two, or even three strong characters would twist the crank while swearing liberally, and the big radial engine would usually start.

Now, if it was possible to hand crank those big, balky engines into action, we believe that it is possible to crank most modern marine gas engines in a dire emergency. But a good crank is required. If it is impossible to do the job with a directly connected crank, then maybe there should be a geared crank available, like that used on aircraft engines.

(*Note*: Perhaps someone will now go into the business of manufacturing good hand cranks for marine engines and will become wealthy at this ancient trade.)

The conventional automotive-type electric starter has much to recommend it. It is simple, easily repaired and, under most circumstances, it starts engines quickly. Its main drawbacks are that it is useless if batteries are discharged, and in extremely cold weather it is incapable of cranking diesel engines rapidly enough or long enough for reliable starts.

The electric starters applied to large, modern outboard motors are essentially the same breed as on automobiles and inboard marine engines. These starters have a pinion drive which meshes a flywheel gear and spins the outboard into action.

Because of their small size and fierce power, electric-starter motors are not highly efficient; this is particularly true of 6-volt starters. Due to low electrical efficiency, starter motors will heat severely if operated for prolonged periods without rest. If extended cranking is necessary, as when trying to fire up a balky engine in cold weather, the best procedure is to crank for 5 to 10 seconds, then allow a 2 minute intermission for starter cooling. Incidentally, this procedure will give the storage battery a chance to recoup its vitality and will result in longer total cranking time from a given charge.

The essential parts of the regular electric starting system (Fig. 54) are battery, cables, switch, motor and drive. In many instances the switch is a remotely operated solenoid, in turn operated by a light-duty push-button switch. The battery or batteries should be husky enough for prolonged cranking, and the battery cables must be of fat diameter and as short as possible. Long, stringy, corroded battery cables cause just as much hard starting

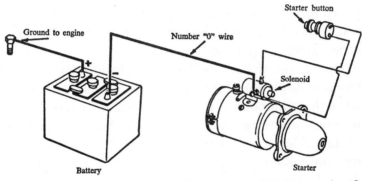

Fig. 54. *Common 6-volt electric starter with push button switch and solenoid relay.*

as weak, inadequate batteries. Even though the battery is new, vigorous and fully charged, it cannot spin the starter snappily through rotten or long, stringy cables because voltage drop through the conductors will be excessive.

Electric starter operation is simple: The switch completes the circuit from battery to starter motor; the motor spins suddenly with the first surge of juice. The business end of the starter has a small pinion gear mounted on a spiral or helical shaft. The sudden shaft rotational acceleration and inertia of the pinion gear cause said gear to slide forward on the shaft and mesh with a large gear on the periphery of the flywheel. When the engine fires, the flywheel speeds faster than the starter pinion, it accelerates the pinion, and the little gear screw itself backs away from the flywheel.

Occasionally, when batteries are weak, a whirring, spinning noise may be heard from the starter, but the engine is not cranked. This happens when batteries are too weak to accelerate the motor with enough snap to screw the pinion forward for flywheel engagement. It may also happen with fully charged batteries if the helical shaft becomes rusty or gummy.

Trouble-shooting on the house cat electric starting system is quite simple. If the starter fails to crank the engine when the starter button is pushed, trouble shooting should start with a check on battery condition, then an inspection of the cables, a test of switch or solenoid, and a look at the connections throughout the system. If it is apparent that full voltage is available at starter motor terminal, then it is probable that the starter has bad brushes, an open winding or broken internal connection. Usually, the best treatment for a defective starter is to haul it to an automotive supply house and have it rebuilt, or swap it for a new one.

Most gasoline marine engines start reasonably well at temperatures well below freezing, but when cold weather starting does become a problem, the starting system needs help. Boats used in cold weather should have lavish battery capacity and the beefiest possible battery cables. The crankcase oil should be of lightest allowable viscosity (usually S.A.E. No. 10W). The ignition system must be in tiptop condition, and it is helpful in a tough cold start situation to energize the ignition system from a separate, fresh battery hooked to ignition only, not the battery which is struggling to crank the frigid engine. If the engine has been out of use for several weeks, it is helpful to pour gasoline into the carburetor float bowl, thus bringing it to correct level and avoiding cranking only to operate the fuel pump.

Sometimes it is a help to prime the engine with gasoline poured into the air intake, and in extreme cases a little ether can be squirted into the intake as the engine is cranked. If you use ether, however, be careful; too much can ruin the engine, and inhaling too much vapor can ruin you. Ether for cold weather starting may be purchased in automotive supply houses, particularly the ones that handle diesel supplies. It comes in little capsules which look like an overgrown vitamin pull. When you are ready to use the pill, puncture it with a pin and squirt a fine stream into the air intake.

Marine diesels are fussy about starting when temperatures fall below $+ 40°$ or $+ 50°$ F. and starting aids are frequently employed to speed chilly starts.

General Motors diesels may be equipped with a small, compact, hand operated oil burner which heats the air box just prior to starting and for the first few minutes of operation (Fig. 55). The burner is a little hand pump, a nozzle and a spark plug; a miniature oil furnace. The hand pump is operated slowly to force a fine mist of oil past the spark. The spark ignites the oil and the hot fire quickly warms the air box and the breathing air passing to the cylinders.

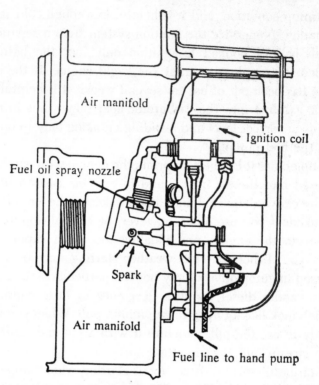

Fig. 55. *Intake air heater available as a cold starting aid on General Motors diesels.*

Many diesels are fitted with glow plugs to help the engine fire quickly in chilly weather. A glow plug looks quite like a spark plug, but in place of spark gap it has a small electric heating coil like an automobile cigar lighter. Prior to a cold start, the glow plugs are energized for a few seconds and then are kept operating while the engine is cranked.

Glow plugs, of course, provide a hot spot to help ignite

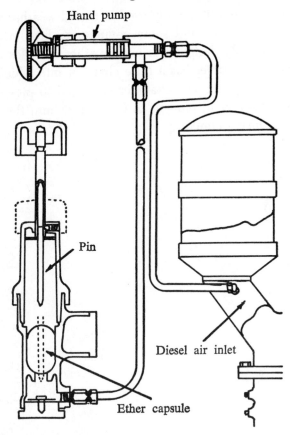

Hand pump

Pin

Diesel air inlet

Ether capsule

Fig. 56. *Ether priming system is another cold weather starting aid for General Motors diesels.*

the diesel fuel as it is sprayed into the combustion chamber. The diesel engine has no spark plugs and depends entirely upon the heat of compression to ignite its fuel. That is why diesels are more difficult to start in chilly weather.

Liquid ether is frequently used as a cold weather starting aid for diesels, and some engines are fitted with a primer assembly designed to handle ether capsules (Fig. 56). An ether primer has a little chamber into which the capsule is dropped. The chamber has a pin to pierce the capsule and a small plunger to force ether into the inlet manifold during cranking.

Chapter Nine

COMMISSIONING THE GASOLINE ENGINE

BELIEVE IT OR NOT, your boat's engine lost weight during the long, dreary winter months. No, it was not doing slimming exercises; it was rusting away quietly in the dank, clammy bilge atmosphere all winter while you enjoyed hot toddies by the cheering fireside. After you scrape off the bits of rust in the spring, the engine will actually be a few grams lighter, but certainly no healthier than when bedded down in the fall.

Revive the engine. Give it several hours of fitting-out treatments and your efforts will be amply repaid in terms of smooth performance and added reliability during the boating season. Before the active season starts is the time to fix machinery which was troublesome last year, and to perform sensible preventive maintenance as a basis for operating with confidence during the summer. Give the engine a thorough servicing with particular attention to lubrication and the electrical system. You will be glad you did.

Start your revitalizing campaign by changing the crankcase oil. True, the oil has not worn out and it has not lost lubricating qualities, but chances are that it is filthy with sludge and gum, it is probably acid and may even contain water. Pump every bit of oil out of the crankcase, then re-place the oil filter element with a good, clean cartridge; a clean oil filter is important to your engine's longevity.

If you want to do an especially good job on the oil, pour several quarts of No. 10 oil into the crankcase after sucking out the dirty lubricant; run the engine for a few minutes, then pump out the No. 10 oil and throw it away. The light oil will act as a flush, removing additional glop from the engine's intestines. Never use kerosene or solvent as a flush; it is bad for bearing surfaces.

And please, sir, do not throw waste oil overboard. It is against the law. It befouls the water, kills fish, dirties hulls, repulses swimmers and defeats the efforts of con-servationists.

Oil is the spring tonic needed by the engine accessor-ies such as water pump, distributor, generator and power takeoff. Some locations are served by grease cup and some by oil cap. Snoop.all around the engine and give a shot of oil or blob of grease as required. Remove the distribu-tor cap and put a few drops of engine oil on the felt wick under the rotor arm, but be careful not to get oil on the breaker points. Put just a tiny dab of grease on the cam inside the distributor; the cam which opens and closes the points.

Take the oil can firmly in hand and lubricate all the control levers, cables, knobs, push rods, bell cranks and similar rubbing surfaces; be sure to include the steering mechanism. Immediately behind the steering wheel on many newer powerboats there is a gearbox containing reduction gears and right-angle drive. Remove the oil filter plug from the gearbox and top-up with heavy engine oil or automobile differential lubricant.

Give the tachometer cable a spring treat. Disconnect it at the tachometer end (use pliers but gently) and pour some light engine oil into the tachometer cable; this lubricant will seep down the length of the sheath, fight rust, and add years to the life of the assembly.

Spring is a good time to inagurate a rust prevention campaign. Use an oily rag or one of those aerosol spray oil cans and give the entire engine and clutch a good buffing, leaving it with a thin coat of oil. Do this two or three times a year to help your engine look nice, shipshape and Bristol fashion. A rusty engine contributes naught to the re-sale value of a yacht, and nothing to ownership pride.

Take a gander at the rubber hoses incorporated in the engine's cooling system (Fig. 57). Are they new looking and free of cracks or kinks? Unless the hoses are in prime condition, now is the time to renew them. Remember, this is a safety measure, too, because a broken hose on the cooling water intake fitting can sink your boat. More than one yacht has gone to Davy's locker because of a broken hose below the water line: a supposedly innocuous hose attached to toilet, sink or engine. Secure your boat against this danger; inspect the hose now.

Sea cocks installed on below-waterline fittings are put there to lessen the danger of sinking in the event of hose or water pipe rupture. If your boat is fitted with sea cocks, by all means make it one of your fitting-out chores to lubricate the cocks and to be sure that they are easily

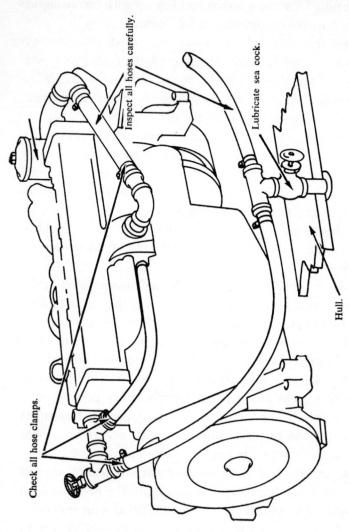

Inspect all hoses carefully.

Lubricate sea cock.

Hull.

Check all hose clamps.

Fig. 57. A rotted water hose or an inoperative sea cock can sink your boat. Service these critical accessories carefully.

operated. Many otherwise shipshape yachts have sea cocks which are useless in an emergency because they are nothing but a mass of rust or corrosion. It is easy to service and check sea cocks while the boat is on the ways, but almost impossible when the vessel is afloat.

Now turn your attention to the engine's electrical system. A few minutes of preventive maintenance on the electrical accessories at springtime may contribute much to your boating enjoyment during the season.

How long have the spark plugs been in use? If they are more than two seasons old or look like hexagonal rust heaps, it is time to change to new plugs. Before removing the old plugs, scrape and blow away all the dirt in the cylinder head plug recesses so that grit does not fall into the cylinder when the plugs are removed. Naturally, new plugs should be of the correct type and should be installed with new gaskets. The plugs should be snugged up firmly but not over-tightened. If a torque wrench is available, the plugs may be tightened to the engine manufacturer's recommendation, or, if this datum is not handy, use a torque of 25-foot pounds on ordinary 14 MM plugs.

Spark plug gap clearance should be measured and adjusted as part of the spring routine. Consult the engine manual for correct plug gap, and measure it with an inexpensive spark plug tool, available at any auto supply store. If plug gap specifications cannot be obtained, set all the plugs uniformly to 0.030 inch; a safe average.

Good, parallel, clean distributor breaker points are more important to your boat's engine than to your car's because the marine ignition system operates under more adverse conditions. The points are the very trigger of the

ignition system, and unless you know that they are in new
condition, renew them. Do not argue with yourself; buy
new ones. Install a new set of points this spring and keep
the old set aboard as a spare. Putting in new points is an
easy job; just be sure to put in the spring, pigtail and
pivot the way they came out. Most important of all, be
sure to adjust the points to correct clearance. This is important because ignition timing and engine performance
are directly affected by point clearance (Fig. 58).

To adjust ignition points, rotate the engine slowly until

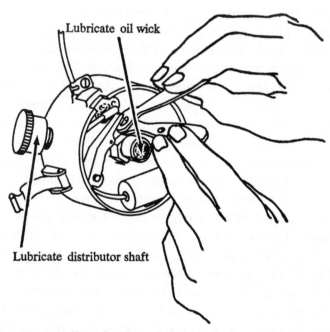

Lubricate oil wick

Lubricate distributor shaft

Fig. 58. *Install and adjust breaker points, lubricate as required and the distributor will give a season of satisfactory
service.*

the points are wide open, then carefully measure the gap between points with a feeler gauge. Make necessary adjustments and tighten the fastenings as required. Try to make the adjustments as accurately as possible because excess point clearance can cause uneven high speed operation; scant clearance can result in hard starting and missing at all speeds.

While you are installing new points, dig down and spend an extra dollar and install a new condenser at the same time; just added assurance of hot ignition. Do not throw the old one away unless you know it is defective. Keep it on board as a spare. It is one ignition component which cannot be improvised in an emergency.

After new points and condenser have been installed, refer to the appropriate timing marks and adjust ignition timing if necessary. Refer to the engine manual for details and method; they vary from one machine to another. Remember, excess spark advance causes "knock," rough operation, uneven idling. Retarded spark results in power loss, high speed miss, burning of exhaust valves and engine overheating.

If your engine is one of the new, high power, high speed V-8's, be particularly careful to time it in accordance with the engine manual specifications. These "hot" engines may be damaged by improper spark timing.

A pleasant, sunny, fitting-out day in spring is just the time to take a long critical look at the ignition wiring, particularly the high voltage wires which run from spark coil to distributor, thence to spark plugs. If the wire insulation is old, cracked and looks like dishpan hands, get rid of it. Poor quality wire can cause hard starting, particularly in damp weather, and can make the engine miss, lose power and generally misbehave.

After the ignition system has been given a good spring tuning, coat it with an anti-dampness compound (Fig. 59). This may be bought at most automotive supply stores, and is usually a liquid spray. Coat all wires, particularly the high voltage wires, and also spray the igni-

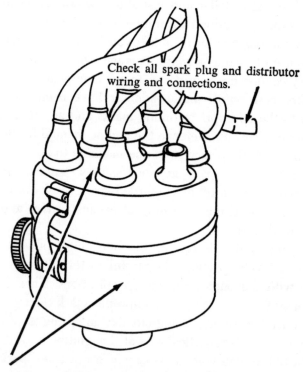

Check all spark plug and distributor wiring and connections.

Coat all surfaces and wiring with silicone.

Fig. 59. *The ignition system will perform better in damp weather if given a light coating of silicone compound.*

tion coil and distributor. This coating will be a blessing
some day this season when the engine is cold and damp
during foggy, wet weather. Under these conditions, ignition systems frequently throw in the towel, but the insulating film will help your engine retain its hot spark
(Fig. 60).

Generator.

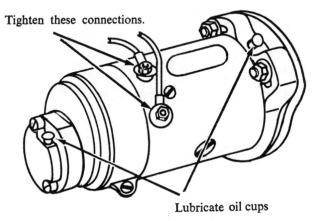

Fig. 60. *The generator's spring tonic should consist of lubricating oil and secure connections.*

Most marine engines of recent vintage have a generator
with external voltage and current control. If the control
functions properly, charging starts at a relatively high
rate on the discharged battery, then tapers to a trickle. If
additional load is placed on the battery, the charge rate
goes up to compensate the added drain, and you can quite
well judge the activity of the voltage control by watching
the ammeter. If your engine batteries always seem partly

discharged in spite of sufficient generator operation, or if they seem to be overcharged and require excess water, these may be signs that the regulator is mal-functioning. In this case, do one of two things: either take the regulator to a repair station and have it checked, or turn it in and

Clean and brighten these surfaces
before assembling clamps.

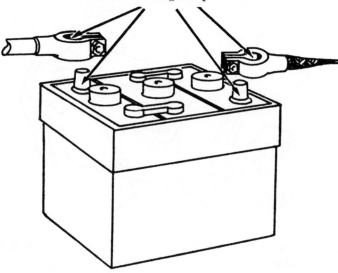

Fig. 61 *The finest battery is no better than its cable connections.*

get a new one. Do not try to adjust the device as it is hard enough to do even with the necessary special equipment.

It almost goes without saying that if the batteries were left in the boat all winter without attention, you are going to invest in new ones. However, if the batteries are in apparently good condition, give them a good charge; carefully clean the outer surfaces with water and baking soda to remove traces of acid. Clean the terminals with a wire brush, and the unit is ready for business (Fig. 61).

Before installing the batteries, take a careful squint at the battery cables. If they are corroded and shabby looking, replace them. No matter how powerful the battery, quick engine starts are impossible with thin, ratty cables. When you purchase new cables, be sure they are of heavy gauge; thin cables cause excess voltage drop and slow starts.

Fitting out also means "cleaning out" and one important accessory to clean is the fuel line strainer or settling bowl. Put a catch pan under the fuel strainer (to keep fuel out of the bilge) and drain it completely. Clean the element of the strainer, install a new gasket if required, then button it up.

Remove the drain plug from the bottom of the carburetor float bowl and drain the gasoline into a catch pan, but be careful not to drip gasoline into the bilge. Do not be too surprised if the carburetor is dry; all the fuel may have evaporated during the long, dormant winter months.

The first engine start of the season is sometimes a hard one because the gasoline system is dry. The firing-up can be made quicker if the engine is carefully primed with a little gasoline. If the engine has a downdraft carburetor, squirt a little gasoline into the throat while cranking. A little gasoline may be poured into the upturned throat of a marine updraft carburetor and the engine will be primed through the syphon tube.

If the gasoline system has tended to gum, or if there are sticking valves after spring starting, there is a spring tonic which may help considerably. Go to a gasoline station and buy several cans of fuel system anti-freeze sold under various trade names such as Dry-Gas. These powerful solvents will remove gum and sludge from the fuel system and will help clear up sticking valves. Run the engine, and while it is running slowly pour the solvent into the fuel line on the suction side of the fuel pump. The engine will actually operate on the solvent as a fuel, and during operation the solvent will clean fuel lines, pump, carburetor, manifold and value stems.

The fact that most fuel solvent containers are shaped like beer cans may suggest that you now repair to the club porch and quietly contemplate the good work you have done.

Chapter Ten

GASOLINE ENGINE TUNE-UP

TUNING an engine is a little like tuning a piano. It takes a good ear and a careful touch. Tuning is an art, yet borders on science; it has rules, yet depends on judgment. One man can tune an engine according to the book, yet another may tune by keen senses and do a better job. As with all mechanical work, common sense is important, detail knowledge is a help and patience is essential. Luck helps.

Engine tuning is satisfying work because the rewards are immediate: A good tuning job makes your engine run smoother, sound better, operate more economically and safer. There is peace of mind in operating a boat with well tuned and adjusted engine, an engine less likely to quit during emergency at the very time when most needed. And there is a sense of pride in operating a velvety smooth engine which you have tuned yourself and have confidence in.

The key to good tuning is sytem: Repair or adjust only one component at a time and test the results of the work before going to the next operation. If two components are adjusted simultaneously and the engine then responds poorly, time is wasted in finding which of the two adjustments is faulty. Furthermore, a false assumption at this stage of the game will compound the felony because you are likely to upset the correct adjustment instead of the faulty one. Make a rule that you will adjust only one thing at a time and will check results before proceeding. Stick to the rule.

Most of the following steps have been described and more fully explained in previous chapters. Here they are repeated in the order in which they will be used in tuning your engine. See how many you remember as they are briefly repeated in this chapter.

Most engines respond well to careful tuning, but if the engine is badly worn and suffers from leaky valves, worn rings, loose bearings and wheezy gaskets, it requires overhaul, not tuning. If the engine is worn and downright junky, tuning is a waste of time and the best procedure is to remove the engine from the boat and send it to a shop for complete re-build. However, if the motor is reasonably sound mechanically, but seems to lack spunk, tuning is the right medicine.

By fair means or foul, get a copy of the engine operation and maintenance manual prior to tuning. This book is a gold mine of information and, as a matter of fact, it is all but impossible to do a perfect tune job without this bible. Write the engine manufacturer and order your book. Be sure to give engine model, year and serial number.

Start the tuning of a four-cycle engine by adjusting valve tappet clearance (Fig. 62). The engine book will tell whether to adjust with engine hot or cold and will specify the correct spacing. Use a good feeler gauge and adjust carefully. Tighten the jam nuts firmly so that the adjustment will be maintained. Use special care when working on worn engines; sometimes the cams and followers wear unevenly so that valve clearance actually varies as the cam follower rotates. Set the clearance correctly, then rotate the follower a complete revolution with your finger; the clearance should remain essentially constant through all degress of rotation. If not, set clearance

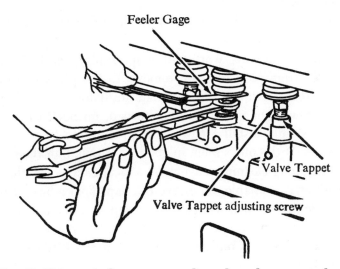

Feeler Gage

Valve Tappet

Valve Tappet adjusting screw

Fig. 62. *Using a feeler gauge to adjust the valve tappet clearance on an L-head engine.*

to specified gap when follower is closest to the valve. Remember, it is better to have excess valve clearance than too little. Insufficient clearance causes poor compression, rough running and burned valves.

When adjusting a valve, be dead certain that the valve is tightly seated and that the cam nose is pointing downward, away from the follower, not pushing against the follower. To assure that the cam is positioned correctly, watch the valve stem, crank engine slowly until the valve settles home in its seat, then continue to crank the engine another half revolution. Now adjust the valve.

When you button up the engine after valve adjustment, use a new gasket on the valve cover, or if a new gasket is not available, use a compound such as Permatex to assure a good seal.

Leaky gaskets let oil drip into the bilge and cause a dangerous mess.

Follow the valve work with a spark plug check: Blow all dirt from plug recesses, remove all the plugs and inspect the electrodes and porcelain insulator. If the plugs look downright miserable and burned, do not fool with them; simply install a new set complete with fresh, new gaskets. If the plugs seem in good condition, buff them in a spark plug cleaning machine at a local garage, test them if tester is available, then give the gaps final adjustment. The engine manual will give exact gap. If a manual is not available, gap the plugs 0.025 inch and install with correct tightness. (Considerable detail on spark plugs was given in chapter 7.)

Turn your attention to the high voltage wires which run from distributor or magneto to the spark plugs. These wires carry more than 10,000 volts, and if improperly serviced can ruin the tune of an engine. Be sure the wires are insulated with fresh, springy material, free of cracks, voids or breaks through which spark voltage might leak. If the wires look sad, replace them. If the wires look good, wipe them clean with a dry cloth then give them a thin coat of silicone compound, a material available at most auto supply stores.

Lead dress or the arrangement of spark plug wires or cables is important, particularly on newer, high compression engines which have elevated spark voltage. The wires should run from distributor to plug directly and in the open, not through conduit or metal guides. The wires must not be cabled, harnessed or taped together in parallel. Where the wires run parallel, they must be spaced; this is particularly true where two plug wires are attached to consecutive firing cylinders.

The reason for careful lead dress and avoidance of bunching wires in close parallel relation is that the surge of high voltage in one wire can actually induce voltage in the adjacent wire, voltage high enough to fire the wrong plug. It is obvious that if the wires induce voltages in each other, the ignition pattern becomes chaotic: Some plugs will fire when they should be quiet and others will be robbed of full voltage. These troubles will affect the engine grievously at advanced throttle, consequently, bunched wires and poor lead dress must be eliminated; this is part of tuning for maximum high speed performance.

A spark plug is somewhat like a vacuum tube rectifier, the center electrode being the cathode, the shell representing the plate. If negative voltage is applied to plug terminal, spark will jump easier than if positive voltage is applied, therefore polarity of the high voltage ignition current should be negative. Engineers at the laboratory of Champion Spark Plug Company determined that it requires about 40 per cent more positive voltage to fire a plug than negative voltage. They also found that many marine engines are wired backward and their plugs receive positive voltage pulses, pulses which render poor ignition and hard starting.

Test your engine to be sure that coil polarity results in negative voltage at the plug wire. The simplest way is to beg, borrow or steal a high reading voltmeter, the type used by television service men. Set the meter polarity switch so that the needle will swing up-scale when the probe touches a negative terminal. Hook the common lead to engine block, run the engine under its own steam,

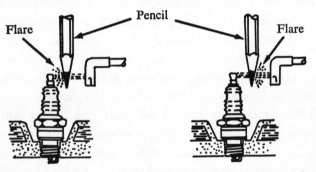

Fig. 63. *How to test a spark polarity with a lead pencil. The left plug, with flare toward terminal, has correct polarity.*

then touch probe to a spark plug terminal; the needle should kick up-scale. If it moves down-scale, polarity is incorrect. The same test may be made with low voltage meter by pressing the probe against the wire insulation near the plug; there will be enough voltage leak to move the needle.

Still another technique of polarity test is shown in Fig. 63. The ignition wire is held about ¼ inch from plug terminal with engine idling, then a lead pencil point is inserted in the arc. If spark flares or feathers with slight orange tinge on the plug side of the pencil lead, polarity is correct. Flare toward the ignition wire indicates backward polarity.

Now, then, what to do if you find your engine wired backward? Interchange the low voltage leads on ignition coil: Put battery wire where distributor lead was, and distributor wire where battery lead was. Simple.

Some ignition coils have their low voltage terminals marked with "pos." and "neg." or with a plus sign for positive and minus for negative. Correct polarity is easy: With negative grounded battery system, the negative (minus) coil terminal is attached to the distributor. In the positive ground battery arrangement, positive (plus) coil terminal is connected to distributor.

After polarity testing, open up the distributor and take a careful look at the points. If they are burned and pitted, remove them and install a new set. A set of points does not cost much and it is hardly worth trying to resurface the old ones. Besides, the used ones are handy to have aboard as spares. After installing the fresh points, carefully adjust gap clearance as specified in the engine book. The right gap is important and has a close bearing upon the entire ignition system's health. Before buttoning up the distributor, rub a minute dab of lubricant on the breaker cam; this will reduce rate of cam follower wear. Remember, as cam follower wears, point clearance is reduced and spark is retarded.

Time the spark immediately after installing and adjusting the points. Dickering with the points will have altered spark timing, so now is the time to set it right. The engine manual gives method of timing and tells where timing marks are. Be careful. The precise instant at which points open is simply determined by a light bulb or meter in series with the low voltage ignition wiring.

A timing light is useful for testing engine timing, and provides an operating check on the automatic ignition advance while the engine is running at various speeds. Most engine manuals specify what ignition advance should be at several tabulated speeds. This test, of course, is only as accurate as the tachometer used to count the engine revolutions.

After the engine has been timed by the book, use your ear to see if you think it sounds just right. A keen tuning merchant can hear an engine which is badly retarded or overly advanced. If you want to practice a little, purposely advance and retard the spark beyond normal limits and listen to the difference in purrs and growls. But do not overdo it. Save the pieces.

A warning: Newer, high speed, high compression engines must be timed with special care. Time the engine by the book and beware of shoving the spark ahead excessively just because more advance gives more speed. Most of the modern, hot engines have compact, efficient combustion chambers which, when used with good gasoline, prevent detonation. These engines will not knock with advanced spark, hence there is no ping to warn that the spark is too far advanced, and the mechanic tuning by ear may be fooled into using timing which will damage the engine.

Warm the engine fully. Run the boat to open water and run at full throttle for a minute or two. If the engine pings or knocks, retard the spark just enough to kill detonation.

This final adjustment should be made while burning the grade of gasoline generally used.

Good, clean, hot, accurately timed ignition has a profound effect on engine performance, and for this reason the tune-up man is justified in spending considerable time attending to the ignition system. There are fine points of tuning unearthed by experience and with new instruments. Uneven distributor cam wear, point bounce, cross firing, leakage paths, intermittent connections and other elusive troubles can be detected by an ignition analyzer, an instrument which looks like a miniature televison set and which may be built from a Heathkit for modest investment. The instrument and handbook that go with it are valuable tuning tools.

A well tuned engine should start easily, even in chilly weather. Prime factors in quick starting are a fine battery, healthy battery cables and good starting switch or solenoid. Test the battery with hydrometer or battery capacity tester. If the battery is old and weak, replace it. Inspect the battery cables; if they are corroded and shabby, replace them. Use a voltmeter and test the cables and switch for voltage drop while the starter is cranking. Voltage drop across the system should not exceed 0.3 volts. If it does, install heavier cables or a better starter switch.

Turn attention, now, to the carburetor. Remove the drain plug from the bottom of the float bowl and drain the gasoline into a tin can or jar (Fig. 64). Be careful. Keep gasoline from dripping into the bilge. The stuff is dangerous. Replace the plug securely and, if possible, pour gasoline into the bowl so that the carburetor will be primed.

Remove the backfire trap from the carburetor air intake. Wash the plates clean, then reassemble the trap on the air inlet. Dirt or lint in the plates of the trap choke the engine, increase gasoline consumption and reduce power (Fig. 65).

Clean and drain the gasoline strainer and trap. Reassemble the trap using a fresh gasket if necessary (Fig. 66).

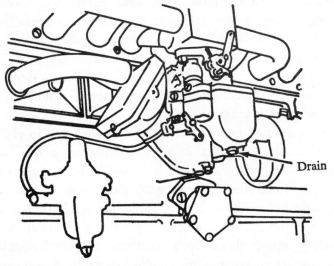

Fig. 64. *Underneath view of an updraft carburetor, showing the float bowl drain plug.*

A good tuning procedure for the entire fuel system including the inlet valves is to run solvent through the entire circuit. An easy way to do this is to feed the solvent into the intake of the fuel pump while running the engine normally. The pump will suck the solvent, push it through the strainer, carburetor, inlet manifold and into the combustion chamber where it will burn. The solvent will remove gum from the entire system and will help free valves which tend to stick. The solvents are similar to lacquer thinner and are sold with trade names such as "Dry-Gas."

When the fuel system is purged and clean, warm the engine fully, then adjust the idle mixture screw on the

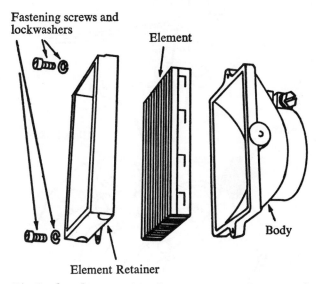

Fastening screws and lockwashers

Element

Element Retainer

Body

Fig. 65. *Explored view of a flame arrester. Tune-up should include cleaning the element; a dirty element chokes the engine.*

carburetor. Some carburetors have double barrels and two idle mixture adjusting screws. Adjust one at a time.

Adjustment of idle mixture is much a matter of tuning by ear. Turn the screw in until the engine runs roughly and acts shaky, then slowly rotate the screw out until the engine clears and rolls along smoothly. On most carburetors, rotating the screw inward leans the mixture, out-

ward enriches it. There is no point in trying to set the mixture extra lean for economy because overall consumption
is but slightly affected by the idle jet.

Adjust idle speed by appropriate rotation of the idle

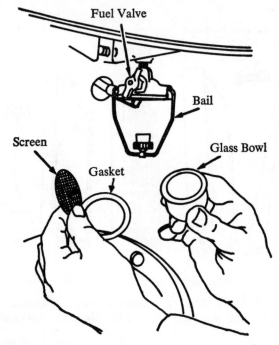

Fig. 66. *Cleaning the gasoline strainer on a small engine. A
new gasket is usually required.*

stop screw, but do not try to see how slowly the engine
will run. Excessively slow idle invites stalling at critical
times (such as when you are about to wallop into a dock)
and speeds fouling of plugs. Most engines are happy with
idling speed between 550 and 750 r.p.m.

Some mechanics like to use a vacuum gauge for tuning the carburetor, particularly for setting idle mixture. (Fig. 67). To use a gauge, attach it to a tapped hole in the inlet manifold, run the engine at idle speed, then set the mixture screw at the position which produces maximum vacuum.

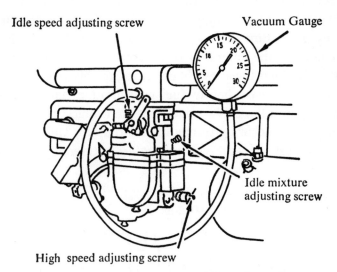

Fig. 67. *Using a vacuum gauge to adjust the carburetor.*

As with most instruments, a vacuum gauge becomes more useful as you get the feel of it. Most vacuum gauges come with a small instruction pamphlet, and when applications are understood, the gauge is a useful tuning tool. Sticking valves, manifold leaks and similar ills can be detected through the antics of the vacuum gauge needle.

Some marine carburetors, particularly updraft ones,

are equipped with a high speed needle valve which adjusts the mixture richness of the main jet. Make adjustments on the main jet cautiously because lean high speed mix may damage the engine. The best procedure for adjustment is to run the boat in open water and operate with throttle advanced. Start adjustments with the needle screwed out several turns, then slowly turn the needle in (leaner) until the engine speed decreases a few revolutions. Then turn the needle back out again (richer) just enough for the engine to recover lost revolutions. When in doubt, tend toward richness. A reasonably rich mixture will not increase hourly fuel consumption notably and cannot harm the engine, but excessive leanness may cause dangerous backfiring through the carburetor and may fry the exhaust valves. Aviation engineers refer to a bit of

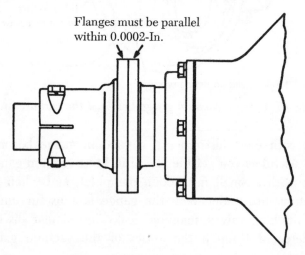

Flanges must be parallel
within 0.0002-In.

Fig. 68. *A smoothly tuned engine requires that the engine and the propeller shaft be aligned perfectly.*

richness as "fuel cooling" because evaporation of a little extra gasoline helps keep an engine's innards comfortable.

Even the well tuned engine will sound miserable if the engine mounts are loose or the engine misaligned. Free the connection at the flanges between engine and propeller shaft and check alignment with a feeler gauge. Alignment of flanges should be true within a few thousandths. If necessary, shift the engine as required to bring about perfect alignment, then be sure the motor is secure in its bed (Fig. 68).

As a final touch to your tuning job, check out all controls; lubricate controls and accessories; take up on packing glands where necessary; give all wiring a close inspection and shine up the engine so that it looks shipshape and proud of itself.

Chapter Eleven

TROUBLE-SHOOTING THE GASOLINE ENGINE

TROUBLE-SHOOTING is the art of diagnosing engine ills and is the aspect of engine mechanics requiring the deepest understanding of engine operation. As in the medical arts, diagnosis requires that the practitioner draw deeply on his knowledge, that he may avoid jumping at conclusions, and that luck be with him.

Sometimes trouble-shooting is a tough job because apparent symptoms are lacking; at other times it is rough because the symptoms all point in another direction, away from the real trouble. But, in general, the trouble can be pinpointed accurately through systematic work and by testing but one component at a time. As with tune-up, scientific system is vital to happy results.

An experienced powerboat man recently growled, "Boats and engines have minds of their own and spend most of their waking hours thinking up ways to tease us. Just when you think you have the whole rig all fixed up perfectly and in swell tune,—blim! The engine will think up a new tormenting grief, generally in the middle of a panic situation. You can't win."

Our friend is right. Machinery can think of the darndest ways to get sick and at the most inopportune, embarrassing moments. Fortunately, however, remote and mysterious troubles are few; the majority of ills can be listed and the cure suggested.

Here are some of the more common troubles which pesky engines present:

Starter Will Not Turn Over. If when you hit the starter switch nothing audible happens, do not attack the starter with pliers and wrench; work backward, backward from storage battery to starter. Do these things in order:

See that the battery is well charged. Test it with hydrometer or capacity cell tester. Closely examine the cable connections on the battery binding posts. Be sure the posts are bright and clean, that the clamps are tight. If connections are poor, cables green and corroded, they will not carry enough current to kick over the starter.

Test the starter switch or solenoid relay by placing a heavy jumper across the switch binding posts. (Be sure jumper is heavy conductor or you may roast your hands.) Examine cable from starter switch to starter binding post; also examine the ground strap from battery to engine block. If all these check out, the starter is getting current. Be sure before continuing.

Put a voltmeter across the terminals of the battery. Hit the starter switch. If the voltmeter drops below 70 per cent of the original reading, either the battery is sick or the starter may be jammed. If the voltmeter does not drop at all, there is an open circuit somewhere. Find it.

Turn your attention to the starter. See that the drive gear is not jammed in mesh with flywheel ring gear. If it is, free it by rocking flywheel manually (ignition off) or by loosening starter mounting lugs. Place voltmeter between starter terminal and frame. Hit the switch; if voltage is normal but the starter makes no effort to rotate, it has internal trouble. Remove it for overhaul.

Starter Motor Rotates but Does Not Crank Engine. This is quite an easy gremlin to catch. First, if the starter spins sluggishly, it probably is not getting enough juice to snap the drive into mesh with the flywheel. Check battery, ca-

If this heavy spring breaks, engine will **not** crank.

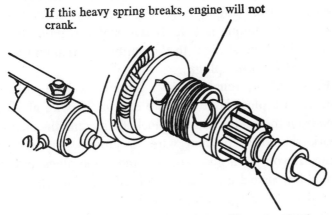

Grease or dirt here will prevent starting

Fig. 69. *Bendix drive on flywheel end of starter.*

bles, switch, ground and connections as previously discussed. However, if the starter winds up with lots of snap but refuses to crank the engine, go straight to the business end of the machine: either the drive mechanism is broken or the spiral shaft is rusty or greasy. If the helical grooves are dirty, clean them so that the pinion can slide freely fore and aft on the shaft and engage the flywheel ring gear properly (Fig. 69).

Engine Cranks but Will Not Start. Surely, this is the

most common of troubles. It usually happens when the wife and kids and guests are all stowed aboard ready for a carefree day afloat. With happy air you hit the starter, the machinery grinds and growls and the battery heads toward exhaustion, all for naught. Not a single healthy response from the balky motor.

Simple things first: Be sure the ignition is on, gas tanks loaded, the fuel valve on, the choke set correctly, the throttle cracked slightly, the engine is not flooded, the operating technique is O.K. If the engine stubbornly refuses to start, go straight to the ignition system and work backward from the plugs.

First, an old reliable trick: Remove a high voltage wire from a plug, hold the bare end of the wire about ¼ inch from the engine head or block, then crank the engine. Spark should snap from wire to ground. Try several plugs. If you get a good spark, remove the plugs and examine for correct gap, excess soot, oil. Set the gaps, clean and dry the plugs and reinstall.

Suppose, though, you got no spark during the test. Then do this: Examine all high voltage spark wiring for dampness and leaks. See that the distributor is dry. The most common single cause of starting failure is dampness. If the whole system appears dank, dry it with a rag, then wet the rag with a little carbon tet and give the distributor, wiring and plugs a rub down. Open the distributor; if it looks damp, dry it out with carbon tet and dry rags. Be sure to give the inside of the distributor cap careful treatment; dampness here will short-circuit the spark.

Test again for spark at the plugs. If still dead, look at the distributor points to be sure that they are opening and closing with reasonable clearance (Fig. 70). Locate the high voltage wire from coil to center of distributor cap. Remove it from the cap and hold the bare end about ¼ inch from the ground. Now open and close the points by finger. Sparks should snap from wire to ground. If not, put

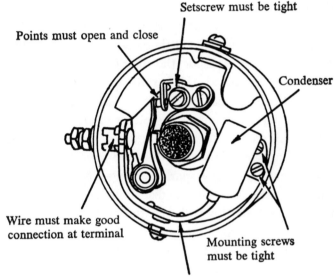

Setscrew must be tight

Points must open and close

Condenser

Wire must make good connection at terminal

Mounting screws must be tight

Look for "shorts" on condenser pigtail lead

Fig. 70. *Distributor with cap removed. Trouble-shooting may include testing point clearance and tightness of connections.*

a voltmeter or light bulb across the points; with points open (separated) there should be battery voltage; the light should light. No voltage? Trace the reason through low voltage wiring, coil primary, terminals, ignition key, fuse, ammeter and so on.

If your test shows voltage across the points, but still no

spark from the coil, lightly sand the point contacts with fine sandpaper. If still no spark, there are only two things left, the condenser and coil. Install a new condenser first, this being the cheaper component. Be sure it is installed correctly in the circuit. If the new condenser does not do the trick, you have eliminated all but the coil. Replace it and you are on your way.

Suppose you find a hot spark on the center wire from coil to distributor cap but little or no spark at the plugs?

Look at the rotor inside the distributor for it may be broken, wet or charred. If the rotor is satisfactory, examine the distributor cap minutely; it may have a microscopic hairline crack containing either carbon or moisture or both. This crack will ground the spark prior to its reaching the plug wires. If you continue to have hot sparks at coil terminal but soggy spark at plugs, replace both the distributor rotor arm and the distributor cap. Chances are a thousand to one this will cure the grief.

We back track now and assume you have hot spark feeding clean, adjusted plugs. Still the engine refuses to start. Look for fuel trouble.

Really now, is there plenty of gasoline in the tank? Be sure.

Work backward from the carburetor, but resist the temptation to attack the carburetor with hammer and screwdriver until you have made several checks.

A couple of simple operations first: See that throttle and choke linkage are working to full limits. Be sure the backfire trap is breathing freely. Know that the gasoline is turned on. Measure the gas supply. When these things have been checked off, try un-flooding the engine. Do this: Place choke in open (running) position; open throttle wide to top speed position; turn ignition on; now crank the engine eight or ten revolutions by starter or hand. If engine tries to fire, reduce throttle setting to about one fourth open and try again.

If the engine still refuses to cooperate, see if the carburetor is getting gas. If gravity feed is used, do this: Shut off the fuel at the tank. Disconnect the fuel line at carburetor connection. Place a container under the open (carburetor) end of the line and crack open the shut-off cock. Gasoline should flow freely out of the open end. If not, you have the answer to the starting problem; the line must be cleaned out. If fuel does flow, shut it off but do not re-connect line to carburetor because it begins to look as though the carburetor may have to come off for a cleaning.

The same procedure is followed for an engine having mechanical fuel pump instead of a gravity system excepting that the engine must be cranked to test for fuel flow. If the pump is working up to snuff, squirts of gasoline should come from the outlet connection while the engine cranks (Fig. 71).

An electric pump is tested by disconnecting the line at the carburetor, then turning on the ignition switch. The pump should pulsate and fuel should flow from the open end of the line. If the pump seems to be working but fuel flow is lacking, it may be that air is being sucked into the line at a break between pump and tank. This frequently happens if there is a fuel strainer or trap in the line and the trap gasket leaks. Investigate these things before condemning the pump.

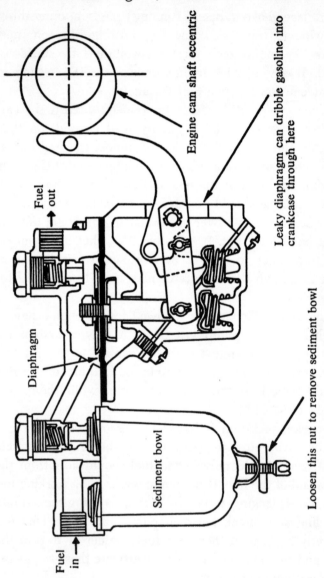

Engine cam shaft eccentric

Leaky diaphragm can dribble gasoline into crankcase through here

Fuel out

Diaphragm

Fuel in

Sediment bowl

Loosen this nut to remove sediment bowl

Fig. 71. *Cross-section view of a mechanical fuel pump.*

If it is perfectly obvious that the carburetor is getting gasoline and spark is hot, perhaps a stuck valve is preventing the engine from starting. Remove all the spark plugs. Crank engine briskly with thumb over the plug holes one at a time. Lack of pressure and suction for one particular cylinder indicates a stuck valve. If compression

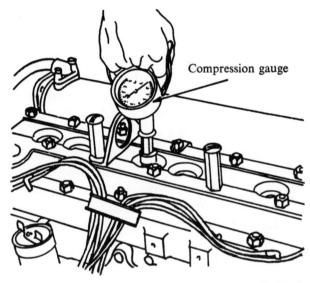

Compression gauge

Fig. 72. *Using a compression gauge to locate a cylinder having a stuck valve.*

gauge is available, the test can be performed even more accurately (Fig. 72). The gauge should read the same within 20 per cent for each cylinder; if one cylinder has a hung valve, the compression gauge will read zero.

When all else fails, when spark, compression and fuel flow have been proven, and the engine is not flooded yet refuses to start, remove the carburetor for cleaning and possible overhaul. Do this last because it is the least likely cause of engine refusing to start.

Rough Idling. This is one of the few cases where we go to the carburetor first. Warm the engine then adjust the idle speed stop screw so that the engine idles at about 600 rpm. Now rotate the idle mixture adjustment slowly in and out until the engine idles most smoothly. On engines having two carburetors or one double-barrel carburetor, each unit must be done individually until the nicest balance is obtained. If rough idling persists after carburetor adjustment, inspect inlet manifold and gaskets for leaks. A manifold leak close to one valve port will make the engine sound as though one plug is misfiring regularly at low speed, then clearing at high speed.

Look at all high voltage ignition wires; check for cracked porcelain on plugs. Be sure plugs are clean, properly gapped. If the engine still idles roughly, use a gauge, set the breaker points, then carefully time the spark. Advanced timing causes rough, hard idling. Keep in mind, though, that while a retarded spark gives a nice tick-tock smooth idle, it will cause overheating and burned valves if overdone.

If everything to this point checks out perfectly, but rough idling remains, adjust valve tappet clearances. If roughness remains, test compression in all cylinders. If compression is reasonably even, then, as a final operation, remove the carburetor and thoroughly clean all internal passage, particularly those in the idling circuit.

High Speed Missing. Go to the spark plugs and work back. Clean and gap the plugs; examine for cracks or burning; replace the plugs if necessary. Check the high-voltage ignition wiring for leaks. Remember, advanced throttle operation causes higher voltage build-up and invites arc-over.

In high-compression engines, particularly the new V-8's, check out the ignition wiring for bunching or parallel lead dress as described in Chapter 10.

If missing hangs on, carefully check out the distributor points, then time the spark. If this does not do the trick, inspect low voltage ignition wires for intermittent contacts.

High-speed miss due to weak mixture or insufficient fuel flow from the pump is easy to detect because it will be accompanied by spitting and popping through the carburetor air inlet. Also, missing due to fuel starvation will cause a softer miss than intermittent spark failure. If this sort of high-speed trouble is apparent, trace the cause of fuel starvation. If the carburetor has high speed mixture adjustment, enrich the mixture. If everything still points to the carburetor, disassemble and clean it. A tiny speck of dirt or fleck of rust in the high speed circuit can cause grief at full throttle.

A few hints on elusive high-speed missing: Excess point clearance may cause high-speed miss but will still give good ignition at lower speed. A loose or faulty condenser may do the same. The ignition coil may have an intermittent high voltage short circuit which will be troublesome at advanced throttle but not at other times. Weakened ignition point spring will allow the points to bounce and raise hob with high-speed performance. Weak valve springs will do the same. Dirty backfire trap will do its worst choking at high speed. Investigate all these things when diagnosing high speed trouble.

Knock or Ping. This is detonation. The sharp metallic click or knock is a trouble easy to shoot.

Ping at advanced throttle is usually caused by excess spark advance, considering the grade of gasoline being used. Knock is also aggravated by weak mixture, by usual overheating or by hot spark plugs and excess carbon in the combustion chamber.

Assuming that spark plugs are correct and mixture is right, ping is eliminated by operating at advanced throttle, engine fully warmed, then retarding spark just enough to kill the knock. But remember, before retarding the spark to eliminate ping, be sure the gasoline grade is what you usually buy, that the cooling system is operating properly and that the spark plugs are of correct heat range.

Backfiring through Carburetor. As a rule, this is an easy trouble to shoot. It is caused by retarded spark or weak mixture or both and is aided by a chilly engine. To get rid of this noisy trouble, be sure that the engine temperature is reasonable, usually 140° F. or higher, have the ignition timed with correct advance, and be sure the carburetor mixture is correct. Some engines will pop back only when the throttle is advanced suddenly. This is because the mixture weakens temporarily at that instant. This symptom points to the carburetor accelerator pump.

If proper mixture and spark setting do not correct popping back, it is possible that the spark plugs are of incorrect heat range. Inspect them for burning or fouling.

It is also possible that a sticking valve or a burned one may cause carburetor backfiring.

Engine Quits, Starts after Short Time. The most probable cause is partial obstruction of fuel line or vapor lock. Look for water, dirt or gum in the system between fuel tank and carburetor. Clean traps and screens. Drain and refill the caburetor float bowl.

Occasionally this trouble is caused by ignition coil or condenser, either of which may operate normally when cool, but have intermittent breakdown when hot.

Intermittent Valve Tap. Valve tapping noise which alternately gets loud then soft, is usually caused by out-of-square valve tappet. As the valve pusher rotates, tappet clearance increases and decreases with intensity of tapping noise following suit. There is no cure for this except overhaul, but provided that clearance is adequate, the noise will do no harm.

Water in Crankcase Oil. If your engine has an oil cooler, be sure all connections and gaskets are good and tight; on small oil coolers, leaks can contaminate the oil. Inspect the head gasket; a bad gasket may allow water to run into a cylinder, thence to the crankcase. If a leaky gasket drips water into a cylinder, some day enough may get in to cause piston breakage due to hydrostatic pressure during cranking. If all gaskets and connections are good, crankcase water is probably caused by a flaw in the engine casting, a trouble which means that major repairs are required.

Gasoline in Crankcase Oil. A worn engine subjected to many cold starts and excess use of choke may suffer

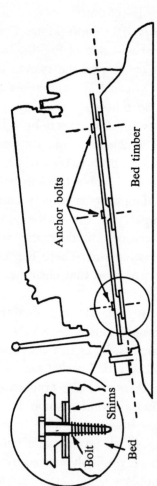

Fig. 73. Loose anchor bolts on engine mounts may cause engine vibration. Tightness should be tested when chasing vibration trouble.

from gasoline dilution of the oil. But on engines having mechanical camshaft-driven fuel pumps, the most common cause is leaky pump diaphragm. The cure is to install a new or rebuilt pump. A badly leaking pump can drip so much gasoline into the crankcase that the oil level will appear to rise on the dip stick. This is dangerous because of possible crankcase explosion (Fig. 71).

Excessive Vibration. A small amount of vibration is expected even from the most perfectly designed and tuned engine. Some hull designs and types of engine mount increase the apparent vibration. If it seems excessive, test the engine mounts for tightness (Fig. 73). If the engine has solid mounts, vibration will be less with correct rubber mounts substituted. But remember that when rubber mounts are installed, the controls, gasoline line, exhaust piping and other connections must be able to accommodate a small increase in engine shake.

Misalignment of engine and propeller shaft will cause

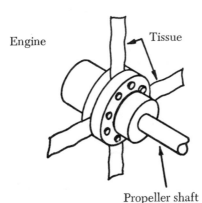

Engine   Tissue

Propeller shaft

Fig. 74. *Misalignment between engine and shaft may cause thumping noises. Alignment can be tested as shown above.*

vibration and thumping; so will loose cap screws or bolts in the flange connection between engine and shaft (Fig. 74). Exhaust piping or other heavy tubing will cause vibration if not properly mounted, preferably with sound insulation from the hull. An unbalanced or damaged propeller will make a noise which will be transmitted to the engine. Sometimes the engine is blamed for vibration actually generated by another component. Therefore, in trouble-shooting, consider the machinery as a complete package, keeping in mind the close relationship.

Above all, stick to your system, do not jump to conclusions and keep Lady Luck on your side.

Chapter Twelve

THE OUTBOARD MOTOR

THE ATTRACTIVELY styled, quiet, brawny outboard motor of the nineteen sixties has a history quite closely paralleling the story of Detroit's shiny chariots. In 1906 when Ole Evinrude was the Henry Ford of the embryo outboard industry, all efforts were directed toward making a kicker which would simply start and keep running. Manufacturers of outboards and horseless carriages had no staffs or stylists, no public opinion pollsters; they had engineers and mechanics sweating to make machinery that would work.

How different the picture today! Outboards and cars are attractively styled, controls and accessories are conveniently arranged and, above all, the machines are unbelievably reliable even when abused and neglected. Both car and outboard motor have had vibration soaked out, exhaust noise muffled to a murmur, starting made mere child's play and operation deceivingly simple.

And while the engineers and mechanics were perfecting the outboard, stylists were knocking off the sharp edges and bright young men were writing enticing ads to sell the new product. Steadily sales increased until about 1954, when the outboard really soared into action with sales figures sky-rocketing and large horsepower motors fire-balling across the boating scene.

A quick cruise through the popular boating waters or a fast gander through any nautical magazine will show the importance of outboard motor boating. As recently as ten years ago most outboard rigs were ten horsepower or less; the boats were small open craft, and outboard water skiing was virtually unknown. But now look: Today's outboard scene abounds in large, nimble runabouts, family cruisers and powerful water ski speedsters. Some of the larger outfits mount two big outboards and deliver 150 whining horsepower through big, husky, deep pitch propellers.

What are some of the design features which elevated the outboard from the putt-putt class and helped it soar squarely alongside the inboard engine as prime marine power? Some features are merely refinements and others are excellent engineering developments, inventions which are as important to the outboard motor as automatic transmissions are to the automobile.

The outboard was given a heady dose of adrenalin hormone when the gear shift was introduced. The introduction of manual shift giving forward, neutral and reverse was essential to getting the outboard on to larger boats, making it safer and attractive to the ladies. Managing a motor without gear shift was difficult and required that the operator sit aft clutching the motor for dear life whilst wrestling with the starter. The boat had to be aimed clear of obstructions prior to firing up, because when it roared into action, the boat surged forward and would wallop anything in its path. Likewise, approaching a pier or mooring demanded considerable skill; the engine had to be konked out at just the right second, there being no reverse to kill embarrassing excess headway.

The outboard engine people have done a magnificent job in reducing exhaust noise almost to the vanishing point. The noise reduction program contributed greatly to popularizing outboard use.

In fact, let's face it: The modern outboard is much quieter than most inboard installations of equal power. Many inboard boats are sold with a loud, roaring exhaust. Perhaps it is time the inboard boat builders took a cue from the outboarders and did some discreet silencing.

Improved electric systems including electric starting boosted the outboard on its way to success. The advantages of effortless starting are obvious, especially when the ladies use a boat, and push-button starting allows the operator to be remote from the engine. Outboards now have powerful generators or alternators and rectifier to re-charge starting and lighting batteries. Many of the systems incorporate automotive type voltage and current regulators to assure even battery charging and to protect the generator against overheating. Some outboards have electric remote controlled choke, an appreciated convenience when the control position is far forward of the engine.

The introduction of bigger engines with three, four or six cylinders helped the outboard on its way to success. Large engines can be used to push big boats and family cruisers, and to tow skiers.

The use of rubber mounting and the incorporation of shock absorbing devices advanced the outboard art considerably. Vibration is so well soaked up and suppressed that a properly mounted outboard on a good, stout boat seems almost like an electric motor. Outboard makers concentrated on noise reduction because silence and smoothness are greatly appreciated by boatmen who cruise any distance or for any length of time.

The majority of motors are two-cycle, multi-cylinder, water-cooled, gasoline burning. But there are exceptions. Some air-cooled outboards are available in smaller horsepower, and there are a few four-cycle machines on the market. Just recently a diesel outboard was introduced, a real diesel which burns furnace oil and has compressed ignition. This little outboard diesel should interest those who like extended cruising in outboard boats.

Let us have a look inside the modern outboard (Fig. 75) and discuss a few specific features by comparing it with typical inboard marine engines:

The most popular outboards have two or four cylinders positioned horizontally and working to spin a vertical crankshaft. This contrasts with the inboard which has vertical cylinders working in conjunction with a horizontal crankshaft. The position of cylinders has little to do with the basic operation of the engine; a vertical shaft is used in outboards simply because the shaft is then lined up with lower unit and a right angle drive is eliminated.

An important difference between four-cycle inboard and two-cycle outboard is the valves. Inboards have cam operated poppet valves, one inlet and one exhaust. The outboard has pressure-operated valves for inlet only and has no exhaust valves; exhaust is through holes or ports cut in the cylinder wall and uncovered by the pis-

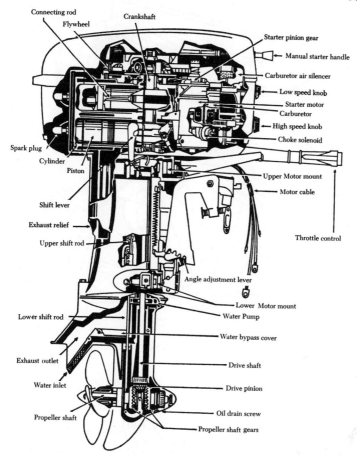

Fig. 75. *Cutaway side view of a modern two cylinder outboard motor equipped with electric starter and electric choke control.*

ton after the power stroke. (See chapter 1.) Most outboard valves are thin reeds or diaphragms placed between the carburetor manifold and the crankcase (Fig. 76) When the piston rises, partial vacuum is created in a sec

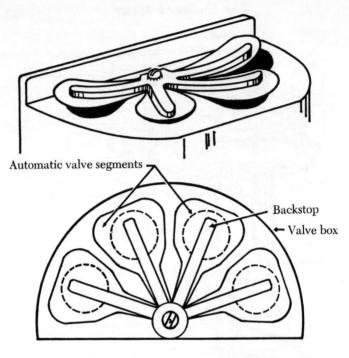

Automatic valve segments

Backstop

← Valve box

Vaporized fuel to crankcase

Closed automatic
Valve box   Valve

Open
← Automatic valve

← Back stop

Vaporized fuel from carburetor

Fig. 76. *Typical inlet valves in a modern outboard engine.*

tion of the crankcase, suction pulls the valve open allowing gasoline/air mixture to flow into the crankcase. When the piston descends, the pressure is created in the crankcase and the automatic valve is forced shut, allowing pressure to rise in the crankcase.

It is obvious, then, that there are no valve timing problems in the outboard. Timing is automatic.

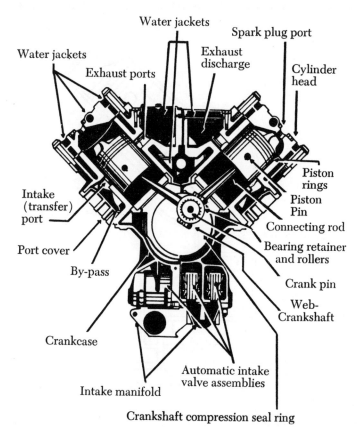

Fig. 77. *Cutaway section of a powerful V-4 outboard motor.*

Internal crankcase construction is much different in an outboard compared to an in-line or V inboard (Fig. 77). The latter type has one large, open crankcase, the bottom being an oil-filled sump or pan. The outboard, however, has a compartmentalized crankcase and carries no oil whatever. Each piston, connecting-rod and crank throw has its own pressure-sealed compartment, because the outboard utilizes crankcase compression to transfer com-

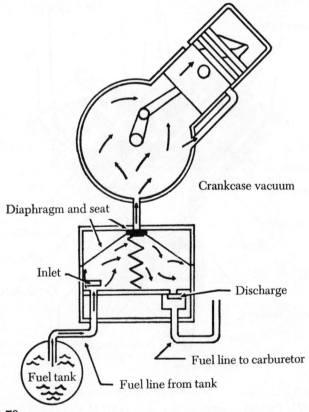

Crankcase vacuum

Diaphragm and seat

Inlet

Discharge

Fuel line to carburetor

Fuel tank

Fuel line from tank

Fig. 78a.

bustible mixture from carburetor to cylinder. This construction points up the reason why outboard fuel must have lubricating oil mixed in: The crankcase is loaded with mixture constantly, and the moving parts depend upon the mixture for lubrication. There is no oil circulated by the pressure pump as in the inboard.

Carburetors and fuel systems on modern outboards are

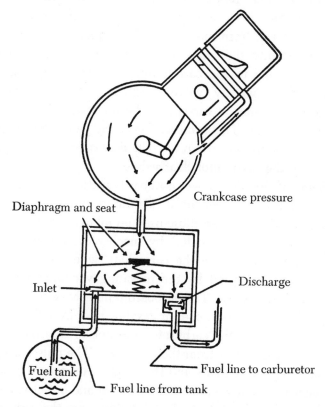

Fig. 78b. *How an outboard motor's fuel pump is operated by the pulsating pressure from the crankcase.*

similar to those on inboard engines, but there are a few exclusive outboard features:

The simplest outboard gasoline system is a small tank mounted right on the power head. With this system, gasoline feeds from the tank to the carburetor by gravity. The arrangement is basic and successful but limited to small motors because of the obvious size limit of the tank.

One popular fuel system uses crankcase pressure to transfer fuel from a portable tank to the carburetor. Two lines run from motor to tank, a pressure line which is tapped into the motor crankcase, and a fuel line to carry gasoline to the carburetor. The system is simple: Through a oneway valve a small portion of crankcase compression is carried to the air space on top the fuel in the tank. This pressure forces the gasoline through the fuel line to the carburetor. The flow is, of course, regulated by the carburetor float valve.

Some of the high-power outboards feature fuel systems incorporating a mechanical diaphram pump. But this pump is different from those used on inboard engines: Inboard pumps are actuated by mechanical linkage to a revolving eccentric on the cam shaft, whereas outboard pumps are energized by the pulsating vacuum/pressure within the crankcase. The outboard pumps have three flexible tube connections: one for gasoline inlet from the tank, one for outlet to the carburetor and one to transfer pressure/vacuum pulses from the crankcase. The pulses cause a diaphragm to oscillate and the diaphram acts as a pump plunger which, in conjunction with inlet and outlet valves, sucks gasoline from the tank and delivers it to the carburetor.

One obvious advantage of an outboard equipped with a fuel pump is that large permanent tanks can be fitted to the boat at remote positions and fuel can be transferred to the motor without the necessity of special pumps, pressurized tanks or other risky makeshifts.

Ignition systems on outboards and inboards are quite similar excepting that outboard motors tend to use magnetos while inboards favor a distributor and coil (Fig. 79).

Magneto ignition is reliable and hot. It has the safety of being independent of the boat's general electric system, hence will function in spite of dead battery, blown fuse or broken wire. Some outboards have a flywheel magneto and some have an individual unit magneto of aircraft type. These latter magnetos are usually driven by a toothed timing belt running between crankshaft and magneto. Naturally, an ordinary V belt cannot be used because creep and slip would throw the engine out of time in a matter of seconds. The angular relation between the magneto drive and the crankshaft determines spark timing of the motor.

The majority of inboard marine engines have automatic spark timing controlled by governor weights in the base of the distributor. Most modern outboards, in contrast, have manual spark advance which is interconnected with the throttle control. As throttle is advanced for more speed, spark is advanced for optimum timing. When the throttle is positioned for starting, spark timing is automatically set at proper position.

Some outboards have a special feature built into the control linkage so that the spark is advanced progressively as the throttle is opened; maximum advance is

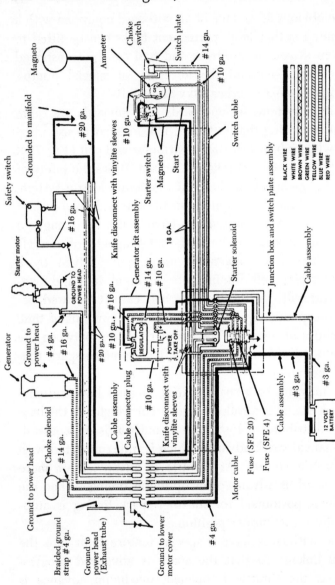

Fig. 79. Wiring of a large outboard motor having an electric starter, a generator, charging regulator, electric choke and other modern features.

reached when the throttle is wide open. However, as the throttle is closed a little, the spark remains at full advance. This feature is aimed mainly at the planing boat wherein full power is applied to get the boat rolling and up on the step, then the throttle can be reduced somewhat with the boat demanding less power but speeding on with full spark advance. This feature is a gas saver.

The electric starters used on modern outboards are almost identical to those used on inboard engines. Of course, since the outboard flywheel is horizontal the starter motor is vertical, but most features are the same as on the inboards. The flywheel has a ring gear and the starter a slidable pinion gear which rides upward to mesh the flywheel gear when the starter button is pressed. When the engine fires, the flywheel speeds up and kicks out the starter pinion. Many outboard manufacturers stress that the starter motor is an intermittent duty accessory and prolonged cranking must be avoided. If a good deal of cranking is necessary, do it at intervals, allowing the starter five or ten minutes to cool between bouts.

Inboard and outboard engines use spark plugs which are roughly similar, but outboards are more fussy about having just the right plug. Also, outboards foul plugs quicker than inboards and should have more frequent plug service. Outboard manufacturers give much attention to recommending just the right plug. Their recommendations are important.

An outboard's lower unit corresponds to transmission, reduction gear, propeller shaft, shaft strut, stuffing box and propeller of the inboard. One of the attractive features of outboard installation is the elimination of separate shafts, struts, stuffing box and rudder which must be installed on the inboard boat.

An important component of the lower unit is the gear shift which gives the modern outboard forward, neutral and reverse (Fig. 80). There are numerous arrangements, but most of the shifts are in the submerged

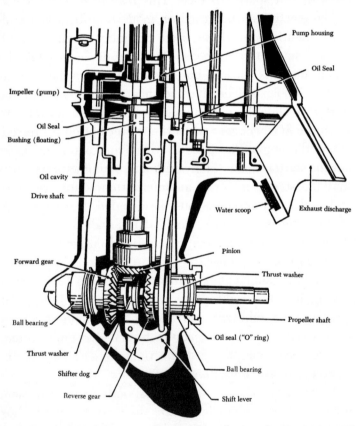

Fig. 80. *Cutaway section of an outboard motor's gear case and part of its lower unit.*

gear case just forward of the propeller. A vertical shaft runs down the unit from the power head; at the lower end is a bevel gear which engages two bevel gears riding on the prop shaft. All gears are in constant mesh. The gears on the propeller shaft rotate freely on the bearings; one gear for forward, the other for reverse. With the shift in neutral, both gears spin freely. In forward, a spline or dog clutch locks the forward gear to the propeller shaft and power is transmitted. For reverse, the other gear is locked to the propeller shaft.

Note that the clutch is a toothed clutch, not a disc or friction device, therefore engagement is positive and instantaneous. Because the engagement grabs solidly, shifting must be done only at slow speed, otherwise the machinery may be torn apart. Most motors have interlocking linkage which makes shifting impossible unless the throttle is near idle. Similarly, many units have an arrangement to prevent engine starts unless the gear is neutral. This is a safety measure.

The use of a splined grabbing clutch is perfectly satisfactory in an outboard motor because the inertia of the rotating parts is so slight that accelerating forces are reasonable. Some motor manufacturers warn against substituting a heavy bronze propeller for the light aluminum one because the added inertia of a bulky propeller might damage the shift clutch.

Some modern outboards have been built with small, efficient differential gear transmission in the lower unit. There are two clutches; when both are released the unit is neutral, when both are locked-up the transmission drives forward, when one is tightened, the pinions rotate and the transmission reverses. This transmission has the advantage of being smoother than others, and can be placed higher in the lower unit to allow a thinner, streamlined shape to the lower gear box.

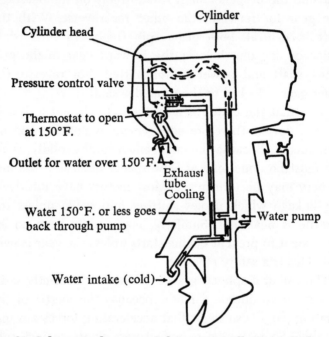

Fig. 81. *Schematic drawing of thermostatically controlled cooling system in a modern outboard.*

Both inboard and outboard engines have cooling water pumps, but their construction and location is different (Fig. 81). Inboard pumps are usually gear or vane type driven through gears or belts from the cam or crankshaft. Most outboard pumps, however, are located down in the lower unit and are driven by the vertical shaft connecting the power head to the lower gear box. Some are vane pumps, some centrifugal and some a combination of the two, utilizing a flexible impeller which operates as a pulsating pump at slow speed, then converts to a centrifugal circulator at higher speed. Some motors utilize the water velocity from the propeller slip stream to force the coolant through the jackets.

Modern outboards and inboards have one thing in common with very similar construction: A cooling water thermostat to maintain jacket temperature at optimum. The thermostat is arranged in the system so that water is recirculated until jacket temperature is normal, then the thermostat reduces the quantity of re-circulated water and increases the flow of "new" water until correct temperature is maintained.

The propeller for inboard installation is usually keyed to a tapered shaft. If a spinning inboard driven propeller wallops an obstruction, something must give; the propeller may dent, the shaft may bend or a strut may warp out of line. To prevent such grief, outboard propellers are protected by means of a shear pin or slipping clutch or both. If the speeding outboard propeller strikes a log or submerged piling, it will shear the pin or slip the protective clutch. Damage is minimized.

Chapter Thirteen

TAKING CARE OF YOUR OUTBOARD

A YOUNG business man, his attractive wife and two small children tumble down the dock, put picnic gear aboard, tidy up the ship and prepare to cast off. Dad touches the starter button, the outboard motor spins eagerly into action, then settles quickly to a pleasant, businesslike bumble. The family casts off, outbound for a carefree day.

Is this a picture conjured up by some advertising copywriter? Not at all. It is a typical true story involving the family outboard motor, a motor given only reasonable, systematic care.

The young fellow pictured above is smart enough to know that all machinery is subject to ills and troubles, and marine machinery in particular seems to have a scheming mind of its own, a mind bent upon harassing the hapless mariner at the most embarrassing moments. The smart motor boat man knows that the best insurance against trouble is constant vigilance coupled with systematic preventive maintenance. Simple maintenance: the oil can, the grease gun, and the sharp eye, inspection kind.

The modern outboard is backed by over four decades of design and manufacturing experience. The machine is well built. Today's outboard is unbelievably reliable, just given recommended lubrication and nominal care.

The first sensible step is to round up a copy of the owner's manual or owner's guide written for your motor. Every new rig comes with one of these instruction booklets. If you do not have a copy of this little bible, or if you lost the original, latch on to a copy. The manual is your motor's best friend.

If you are quite a fair mechanic and feel capable of more extensive maintenance, or if you are curious to know more about the technical details of your motor, buy a copy of the service manual or shop handbook applicable to your machine. This book covers engineering fine points, repair techniques, timing details, clearances, tolerances and overhaul procedures.

Be sensible. Do not try to doctor your motor blindly. Get the book first and find out what the manufacturer has to say about lubrication, tolerances, adjustment and tune-up.

Correct motor installation is a part of motor care. Proper transom height is important because if the motor is mounted too high above the water the propeller will slip, churn and cavitate, making a terrible fuss but doing little useful work. If mounted too close to the water, the motor will drag, kick up excess spray and tend to douse itself in a following sea. Most of the larger outboards require transom height of 15 to 20 inches.

Be sure that the angle or tilt of the motor is just right or the motor will constantly fight the boat, either trying to make the bow plow into the water or trying to suck the stern down. Wrong angle adjustment slows the boat and wastes fuel. Most installations are just right when the lower unit is vertical at full boat speed; but cut and try is the best method of finding the optimum angle (Fig. 82).

Breaking in a new outboard motor amounts to nothing

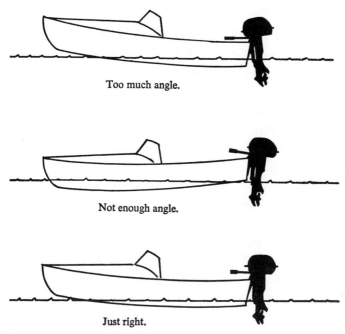

Too much angle.

Not enough angle.

Just right.

Fig. 82. *Proper tilt angle is important. Too much angle makes the stern of the boat suck down; too little makes the bow plow.*

more than running easy for the first hour or two while generally keeping a close eye on the machinery. Do not exceed three quarters throttle during the first hour or two, then gradually work up to full throttle as the engine gains running time. During the first interval of operation, keep an eye on the cooling water outlets to be sure that there is plenty of circulation. Cooling system failure could ruin a motor on its maiden voyage.

Most motor manufacturers recommend normal lubrication during break-in and they warn against the use of special friction reducers, dopes or snake oils during run-in.

All of the popular "name brand" outboards are two-cycle machines having no lubricating oil in the crankcase. The motor's innards, including main bearings, connecting rods and pistons are lubricated by oil mixed with the gasoline. The oil/gasoline ratio varies a little with the engines, but the most popular mix for modern outboards is a quart of oil in six gallons of gas, ⅓ pint per gallon. Use just the right amount of oil: Insufficient oil will cause rapid wear or may even lead to engine seizure. Excess oil causes lots of smelly blue smoke and fouls the spark plugs.

What oil to use? Most motor makers recommend SAE No. 30 automobile engine oil of good grade. However, stay away from high detergent oils because they foul plugs quicker than ordinary oil. In general, the highest detergent oils are the top grade product recommended for diesels and for severe service in four-cycle engines. There are many oils on the marine market prepared specifically by major oil refiners for outboard use. These products, approved by outboard people, are compounded to lubricate efficiently, then burn cleanly with minimum plug fouling.

Modern outboards, even the super power ones, operate happily on regular gasoline. Unlike modern super power cars, they do not require the highest octane gasoline. Either regular automobile gas or marine white is perfectly acceptable. Sometimes a batch of gasoline will tend to form gum or varnish in the outboard and will foul the plugs. In many instances this is the particular batch of gas, not necessarily the brand. Gasoline which has been left standing in storage in tanks or cans will tend to gum. This is particularly true in hot weather.

If you have trouble with gum and fouling, try another brand of gasoline, or try another dealer carrying your favorite brand. The same applies to oil. If you suspect that oil is fouling the plugs, try another brand, or, if you are using automobile oil, switch to special outboard oil and see if things improve. If your motor is going to be unused for several weeks, empty the gasoline tank and carburetor bowl so the fuel will not get stale. (Burn it in your car, the lube oil will not hurt the car engine; might do it some good.)

If you never do another single thing toward maintaining your outboard, at least be religious about lubricating it regularly. Nothing can extend its life more than oil and grease.

Your rig gets its most important lubrication from the oil added to the gasoline. Neglect this and you kill the machine. The second most important lubrication is the heavy oil you squirt into the gearbox at the bottom of the lower unit. Neglect the lower unit, and you suffer expensive repair bills plus possible failure while cruising (Fig. 83).

The gears, bearings, clutch and splines of the lower gearbox operate under severe conditions and are subject to the disadvantage of operating submerged.

Sweating and seepage are inevitable, consequently the oil must fight not only friction but moisture and even salt water. It is obvious, then, that the oil should be changed regularly. Most outboards have a lower plug or drain and an upper plug or vent. Changing oil is a snap: With en-

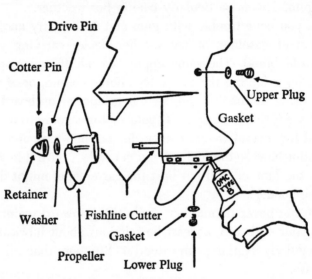

Fig. 83. *The gear box in the outboard motor's lower unit is lubricated by viscous oil squeezed from oversized tubes.*

gine vertical, both plugs are removed and the old lubricant allowed to dribble out of the lower plug. Then a squeeze tube or gun is used to force oil into the case until it flows from the top vent. The upper plug is replaced first while the tube still blocks the lower one; this provides an air lock so the oil cannot ooze out while the lower plug is replaced. That is all there is to it. A simple lubrication job which, done regularly, will add years to the life of any lower unit.

The lower gearboxes of various rigs require different oils, but most modern outfits use SAE No. 90 hypoid oil or OMC type "B" oil. These oils are available from outboard dealers in over-sized toothpaste tubes having spouts designed exactly for the job.

The balance of outboard lubrication is the oil can and grease gun variety designed to limber up such things as throttle linkage, clamp screws and shift mechanism. Each outboard model is a little different, but typical lubrication program is shown by the chart for the Evinrude Big Twin 40:

LUBRICATION POINT	LUBRICANT	FRESH WATER	SALT WATER
Gearcase	OMC type B	50 hours	50 hours
Cam follower and cam	OMC type A	60 days	30 days
Carburetor and magneto linkage	OMC type A	60 days	30 days
Clamp screws	OMC type A	60 days	30 days
Throttle shaft bearing and gears	OMC type A	60 days	30 days
Gear shift lever shaft and lockout	OMC type A	60 days	30 days
Swivel bracket and reverse lock	OMC type A	60 days	30 days
Tilt and trail lock pin	OMC type A	60 days	30 days

To keep your outboard's power head humming, there are four basic things which you can do: Keep spark hot, spark plugs serviced, carburetor adjusted, gasoline fresh and clean.

One prime requisite for a hot spark is clean, dry, well

insulated spark plug wires. If these wires "leak," the spark will be weak and intermittent. If your outfit is several years old and a little weathered, inspect the high voltage wiring with a critical eye and replace it if not perfect. Give the wires a thin coat of anti-dampness compound which you can buy in any automobile parts store. Follow

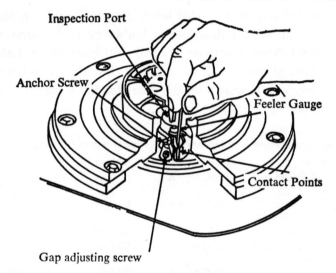

Fig. 84. *Correct adjustment of magneto breaker points contributes greatly to a hot spark.*

through by coating exposed parts of the magneto (or coil) and the spark plugs.

Clean, carefully adjusted breaker points contribute to hot spark (Fig. 84). On many motors, either with magneto or distributor, the points are available for inspection and service. After perhaps 250 hours of operation, or if ignition seems to falter, the breaker points should be inspected, cleaned and adjusted for exact clearance. Detailed procedure for any specific engine is given in the owner's handbook. If the points appear badly pitted and burned, renew them. New points are not expensive; they are a good investment in hot spark.

Regular spark plug service is more important to keen outboard performance than to inboard because outboards are rough on plugs. Use exactly the recommended plugs, clean and adjust gaps regularly, keep outside porcelain dry and always carry a spare set of plugs. Remember to use a good gasket when replacing the plugs. The gasket not only prevents loss of compression but is responsible to help keep the plug electrode at design temperature.

Try not to dicker with the carburetor too much unless you are sure it needs nursing. Lots of troubles are blamed on the carburetor when the trouble is actually something like dirty plugs, weeds on the propeller, clogged fuel line or wet ignition components.

Most power heads have two carburetor adjustments: The high-speed needle valve and the low-speed or idling adjustment. If you have to adjust either, do it after warming the engine completely with a good, hard run. Make one adjustment at a time. Run the boat with open throttle and slowly turn the high speed adjusting screw in or out (right or left) until the engine runs fastest and most smoothly. Close the throttle all the way to idle position and adjust the slow speed needle until the engine runs most smoothly.

Most outboard carburetors have a drain screw or plug on the bottom of the float bowl; some have a float bowl which is easily removed for cleaning. All carburetors are

subject to being slugged with some water or dirt occasionally, therefore it is a good idea to drain the float bowl
or to remove and clean it periodically. Be careful; keep
gasoline drippings out of your boat's bilge.

Many power heads have the gasoline system fitted with
fuel filter and sediment trap (Fig. 85). Regular cleaning
of the filter and draining of the bowl will block water and
grime from the carburetor. It is much easier to service the
fuel filter than to disassemble the carburetor and clean all
the jets, tubes and passages. Anyway, when you reassemble the carburetor it is badly out of adjustment and requires sweat and tears to get cooking nicely again.

One happy day you are perking along, the motor humming merrily; all's well with the world. Suddenly, blim!
you hit a wake, the boat lurches, the outboard falls free
and into the deep brink. It is dunked in umpteen feet of
water. What to do?

Naturally, fish the rig up from the bottom as quickly
as possible and take it to your boathouse or shop. Speed is
important, because the quicker you dry the works, the less
damage will be done.

Remove the shroud or covers. Dump all water and gasoline from the fuel system, including the carburetor. Remove all spark plugs. "Ground" the spark plug wires to
motor block lest you ruin the ignition coil during subsequent operations. Open the throttle wide, then hand
crank the motor slowly in all positions, vertical and on its
sides. Work out as much water as possible. Spray a little
lubricating oil through the spark plug holes and rotate
the flywheel some more. Blow air through all electrical
components with particular attention to the magneto or

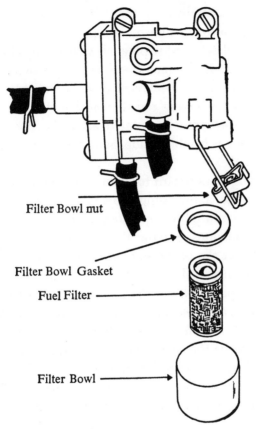

Filter Bowl nut

Filter Bowl Gasket

Fuel Filter ⟶

Filter Bowl ⟶

Fig. 85. *This sketch shows how the fuel filter is disassembled for cleaning.*

distributor. Get the electrical machinery as dry as possible. Be sure the breaker points are dry. Dry the plugs or install new ones; refill with fresh gasoline and try to get the motor going again, the sooner the better.

After the dunked motor starts, run it a good half hour

(in water, naturally) so that all the metal parts are heated up and dry. Finish the operation by lubricating the rig completely and wiping off with an oily cloth.

A warning: If the motor was running when it hit the water, it may have swallowed enough water to bind up and bend a connecting rod. If you detect flywheel binding when the motor is rotated after the plugs are removed, there is trouble inside. Send the motor to the shop for overhaul.

Preparing an outboard for winter storage is easy, and if you complete a few simple operations the engine will hibernate comfortably: Operate the engine in fresh water for a few minutes. Set the throttle at about half speed, then pull out the choke until the engine quits. The rich gas/oil mixture will help lubricate internal parts. Stand the motor upright on the floor, remove the spark plugs and spray a little oil in each cylinder. Turn the engine flywheel to distribute the oil and to drain water from the cooling pump. Replace the spark plugs. Drain the entire fuel system. Remove the propeller, then clean and lubricate the shaft and renew the shear pin if necessary. Finally, wipe off the entire machine with an oily rag to discourage corrosion.

Propeller selection is generally an easy matter for the outboard owner. If the motor is used on an average runabout, the standard propeller is usually adequate (Fig. 86). If your boat is large and slow, you may do better with a lower pitch propeller; if your boat is a fast hydroplane, more pitch will help. An important point is to use a propeller which allows the engine to spin within rated speed range at full throttle. Motor speed can be measured with

portable tachometer. Most modern, high-powered outboards should have full throttle speed between 4,000 rpm.
and 5,000 rpm. Consult the owner's manual.

Getting the most from your outboard is as much a matter of proper use as correct maintenance. Sometimes the

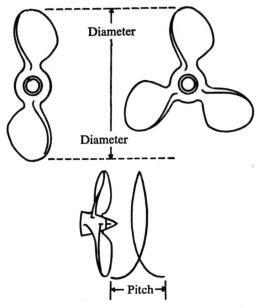

Fig. 86. *This shows the relationship between propeller diameter
and pitch. Motors on fast, speedy boats require more pitch.*

motor is blamed when the operator is actually at fault.
Outboard manufacturers have a few sensible reminders:

1. *Keep the bottom of the boat free of grass and bar-
nacles. A foul bottom robs power, reduces speed and
wastes gasoline.*

2. *Have propeller checked seasonally for pitch and balance.*

3. *On long runs, operate with throttle backed-off from wide open.*

4. *Distribute load in the boat so that the hull rides at best angle.*

5. *In weedy locations, check the propeller frequently for fouling. Clear the blades when necessary.*

Indeed, if you take care of your outboard it will repay the attention by giving many long hours of hard service.

Chapter Fourteen

SMALL BOAT DIESELS

THE BRAWNY little marine diesel has finally hit its stride in pleasure-boat use. The passing years have seen the diesel become smaller, lighter and cheaper to the point where it can now compete for favor with its gasoline burning cousin. Granted on an even horsepower footing the diesel is still heavier, bulkier and more expensive to buy than a gas engine, but the gap is closing and the diesel takes top honors in safety and cheap operation.

In the days when gaff rigs and bowler hats dominated the boating scene, diesel engines were grand piano size and larger; they rotated slowly, worked hard and were used mostly by commercial people. During the nineteen thirties and forties, engineers worked steadily designing small, lighter diesels; then the post war years saw the diesel really blossom. Small, light diesels are now on the market in profusion: There are tiny one-cylinder, air-cooled models, single-cylinder water-cooled units, engines of four, six and eight cylinders delivering power from three horsepower to many hundreds. There is even an outboard diesel on the market.

Because the diesel had its start with the commercial people and because it is popular with builders and users of trucks, bulldozers, power shovels, pumping stations, tug boats and military gear, it is inherently a tough, reliable machine. It resembles its users. It is rugged and practical.

Diesels for boats and yachts are usually built around one of the proven commercial engines. For example, the rugged Gray Marine Diesel is based on The Continental Industrial Diesel. The General Motors Marine Diesel is a version of engines popular in truck and bus. Similarly, Caterpillar Marine Diesels are a close cousin to the mighty earth mover, and Cummins Marine Engines are blood brothers to tough truck engines. Few diesels are born with a silver spoon or nursed on a pink cushion. They work for a living.

High-speed marine diesels can be either two-or-four-cycle machines, water or air cooled, supercharged or normally aspirated. Several builders are resorting to mechanically driven or exhaust turbine driven superchargers to wring more power from a diesel of given size and weight. Super-charging is applied to both two- and four-cycle engines.

An interesting comparison between diesel and gasoline engines may be made by briefly reviewing what takes place inside of each:

The four-cycle gasoline engine (Fig. 1) has four phases of activity as follows:

1. Intake valve is open, piston descends and sucks a combustible mixture of gasoline and air into the cylinder. This is the intake stroke.

2. Both valves are closed for compression stroke during which the piston compresses the fuel/air mixture.

3. Valves remain closed, spark ignition occurs, mixture

is ignited then heat of combustion drives piston down on power stroke.

4. Exhaust valve opens at end of power stroke and remains open while piston rises on exhaust stroke.

Now compare the gasoline engine's four-cycle events with matching events in a diesel (Fig. 3):

1. Intake valve is open, piston descends, sucking in

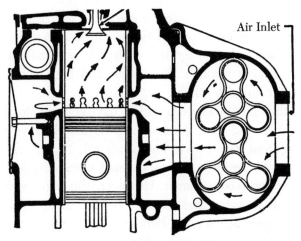

Fig. 87. *Breathing air for this 2 cycle diesel is supplied by a positive displacement rotary blower.*

pure air. The diesel has no carburetor to mix fuel and air.

2. Both valves close for compression stroke and the piston compresses plain air. Compression is extreme and the air is greatly heated.

3. Valves remain closed, a mist of fuel oil is sprayed into the torrid air squeezed within the cylinder, the fuel flashes, and heat of burning drives the piston down on power stroke.

4. Exhaust valve opens at end of power stroke and remains open while piston rises on exhaust stroke.

Notice that there are two important differences between the gas engine and the diesel: The diesel breathes only straight air during intake, while the gasoline engine is sucking fuel/air mixture. Also, the diesel has much higher compression ratio; it squeezes air so fiercely during compression that the air becomes red hot, hot enough to ignite the fuel without the electric spark. Elimination of electric ignition is one of the beauties of marine diesel power. Certainly the ignition system is a prime cause of marine engine troubles. Dampness and high voltage do not cotton to each other.

Gasoline marine engines seldom have compression ratios higher than 8.5 to 1, whereas marine diesels have ratios ranging from 16 to 1 up as high as 20 to 1. The diesel's high compression results in high thermal efficiency, low fuel consumption, cool exhaust. However, the high ratio also stresses the engine and requires beefier parts, thus making the diesel heavier and bulkier than its gasoline cousin.

The passing years have seen diesel and gasoline approaching each other in many ways, but they can never quite come together as one composite machine. There are limits. The diesel started life as a large, slow machine in which fuel was injected for a considerable time interval during power stroke. The power curve looked quite like that of a steam engine. As time passed, engineers speeded up the diesel and made its cycle approach the gasoline engine, with advanced valve timing, earlier, faster fuel injection and fast igniting fuels. At the same time, the gas engine was going up and up in compression ratio with resulting higher efficiencies and lower exhaust temperatures. Some gasoline engines have even gone to a form of fuel injection, but basic differences remain and the twain shall never quite meet.

The gasoline marine engine is limited in compression ratio and thermal efficiency by knock or detonation. Even with fine, anti-knock gasoline the engine will ping badly if compression is too high. As soon as an engine knocks, efficiency falls. It is obvious that if compression ratio is increased to the extent of causing knock, higher compression will decrease efficiency, not increase it.

A gasoline engine is inherently vulnerable to knocking because the full cylinder of explosive mixture is ignited all at once by the spark. If compression is too high, the mixture will overheat and detonate like dynamite rather than burn smoothly.

High compression in a diesel actually reduces the tendency to knock, therefore compression may be as high as desired, commensurate with mechanical limits. The diesel does not suffer from detonation or pinging because during extreme compression there is no fuel mixture in the cylinder to cause trouble. Fuel is sprayed in as a fine mist and burns progressively as it enters the hot, swirling air of the combustion space. The fuel burns instantly as it is squirted in and before an explosive mixture can accumulate in the cylinder. Diesel knock can take place if compression temperature is low or fuel has poor ignition characteristics. These conditions may cause some delay in ignition so that a charge of fuel is injected, fails to ignite immediately, then ignites late after forming a combustible mixture in the cylinder. However, higher compression might cure the trouble, lower compression would aggravate it.

The diesel realizes attractive fuel economy not only from high compression ratio but also from direct injection of fuel into the combustion chamber above the piston. In a good diesel the injection system meters just the precise amount of fuel to each cylinder at the right instant. There is no distribution inequality as in the gasoline engine.

The gasoline marine engine has an inlet manifold which distributes burnable mixture from carburetor to cylinders. Due to tilt of the engine and mechanical in qualities of manifolding, some cylinders get a richer mixture than others. This means waste. The diesel has no distribution problem because fuel is directly injected. But suppose the injection system is unbalanced and one cylinder gets a little more fuel than the others? There is no waste; that cylinder simply works harder.

Diesels operated at part throttle are particularly efficient because less fuel is injected and there is a great excess of air for combustion. It is like running a gas engine on lean mixture, except that the gas engine will quit if the mixture becomes too lean. A diesel just runs slower as fuel quantity is reduced; in fact that is the way the diesel is controlled: more fuel injected for greater power, less for reduced demands. A diesel is stopped either by cutting off the injected fuel or by choking off the air, usually the former.

Marine gasoline engines are much easier to start in cold weather than diesels. This figures: Diesel ignition depends upon heat of compression whereas gasoline ignition is electric, hence independent of engine temperature.

When the diesel's castings and pistons become chilled below a certain temperature, starting becomes a problem and special starting aids are necessary. Low temperature starting aids include electric glow plugs, oil fired heaters and liquid ether injection. (See chapter 8.)

The owner of a marine diesel has no worries about tune-up and trouble-shooting on carburetor or ignition system because the diesel is bare of these accessories. However, the diesel does have an injection system which takes over the function of both carburetor and ignition system (Fig. 88).

The injection system is the most delicate and carefully adjusted bit of the diesel and is the accessory requiring most preventive maintenance. Just as moisture is the enemy of electric ignition, so is dirt the enemy of the injection system. The most important bit of routine diesel care is to keep fuel clean, service fuel filters and change filter elements as required. Like spark plugs in a gasoline engine, diesel injectors are removable for servicing (Fig. 89). Most diesel manufacturers direct that injectors be removed and serviced after every so many hundreds of hours. On most engines this can be done by the mechanically inclined owner if he is equipped with the service tools (Fig. 90).

The reason that dirt is death to the injection systems is that these mechanisms are fitted with such close tolerances and have tiny holes and fine passages. Even the smallest bit of grit or lint can stop an injector, or, worse, may ruin it (Fig. 91).

Injection pressures range to over 10,000 pounds per square inch. Pressures are necessarily terrific in order to

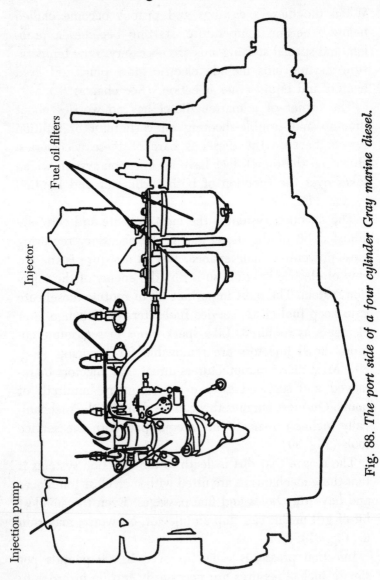

Fuel oil filters

Injector

Injection pump

Fig. 88. The port side of a four cylinder Gray marine diesel.

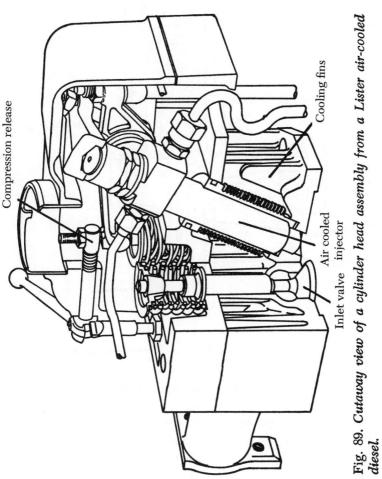

Fig. 89. *Cutaway view of a cylinder head assembly from a Lister air-cooled diesel.*

Compression release

Cooling fins

Air cooled injector

Inlet valve

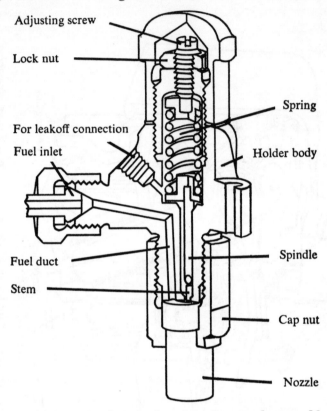

Fig. 90. *A sectional view of an injection nozzle assembly.*

squirt the fuel quickly into a cylinder already under elevated compression pressure. Injection pumps and valves must be closely fitted in order to handle such mighty pressures without leakage. Whereas ordinary engine bearings are fitted with several thousandths inch clearance, injection pumps are fitted with clearance of only several one hundred thousandths, consequently a human hair can jam the pumps. Think what grit can do to such a delicate instrument.

High speed marine diesels, the kind used in pleasure boats, burn fuel oil which is very similar to Number 2 domestic burner oil. In fact furnace oil and diesel fuel are the same excepting that diesel fuel is selected for combustion qualities a little more carefully than the household

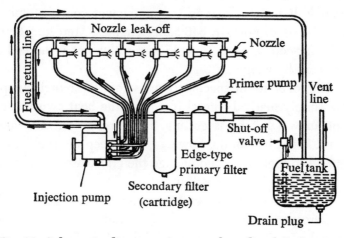

Fig. 91. *Schematic diagram of a complete diesel fuel system.*

product. The Caterpillar people actually recommend the use of domestic furnace oil because it is cheap and the Caterpillar engines thrive on it.

Cetane number of diesel fuel is a little like octane number of gasoline, although the numbers refer to distinctly different qualities. Fuel of high cetane number ignites quickly and contributes to easy starting and smooth running. Sulfur content is an important specification. The content should be as low as possible because sulfur promotes acid formation in fuel and crankcase oil. If it is necessary to use fuel of high sulfur content, frequent crankcase oil changes are important.

For Series 71 marine diesels, General Motors suggests fuel oil cetane number of 40 to 45 or better and sulfur content not to exceed 0.5 per cent. Gray specifies about the same as G.M. Cummins specifies 40 Cetane for J Series Diesels but states that in summer lower cetane number may be used. For MB 846 series engines, Mercedes-Benz calls for cetane of at least 45 and sulfur not to exceed 1 per cent by weight.

The joker to all specifications is that most fuel pumps are simply marked "diesel fuel" and the boat owner does not know what he is getting. He must go on faith and trust. What he can do, however, is to keep the fuel clean, attend to fuel filters and change the crankcase oil often in case the fuel is rich in sulfur.

Most diesels will run on kerosene as an emergency fuel. If kerosene is used, though, lubricating oil should be mixed with it, about a quart of lube oil to five gallons of kerosene. This procedure is desirable because kerosene is thin and has poor lubricating qualities. Untreated kerosene might damage the injection system.

Never try to run a marine diesel on gasoline. The engine will not run, the practice is dangerous and gasoline will ruin the injection system.

A diesel's condition and the quality of its fuel may be judged by the exhaust smoke. A diesel can smoke in three colors, each color indicating a particular condition:

1. Black or dark gray smoke warns of combustion trouble and is usually most apparent at or near the full throttle. It may be caused by fuel of low cetane rating, engine too cool, obstruction in air inlet, dirty or dribbling injectors or poorly timed injection.

2. Blue smoke indicates that the lubricating oil is being burned along with the fuel. As in the gasoline engine, prime causes are worn piston rings, out-of-round cylinders and worn valve guides.

3. White smoke is sometimes called "cold smoke" by diesel men. Generally, it is not smoke at all but is fuel oil mist shot out of the cylinders unburned. White smoke is caused by one or more cylinders misfiring due to low temperature, poor compression, leaky valve or improper timing.

The exhaust of a properly timed and tuned diesel will have the characteristic petroleum odor, but a good diesel using correct fuel need not smoke any more than a gasoline engine.

Diesels are more fussy than gas engines about crankcase lubricating oil because bearing pressures are more severe and acid contamination greater. The diesel owner should try to buy lubricating oil by specification rather than just any can of oil off the shelf: It is usually possible to find which grades and brands of oil meet the required specification. Indeed, some cans are marked with specifications which the oil meets. Also, the oil companies can tell you what specifications their products meet.

Gray Marine calls for lube oil to meet specification MIL-L-9000. For most service, G.M. specifies MIL-L-2104 S-1L. Caterpillar favors MIL-L-2104 Series 3.

Mercedes-Benz advises MIL-L-2104 A and warns against the use of excessively viscous oils. A list of diesel lube oils has been compiled, telling which brands meet specifications. This list is obtainable from Internal Combustion Engine Institute, 210 North Wells Street, Chicago 6, Illinois.

In matters of lubrication and preventive maintenance, the diesel owner's best friend is the engine instruction manual. Caring for a diesel without "the book" is like sailing in the fog.

Most powerboat engines are four-cycle engines (Fig. 92), the type of engine reviewed earlier and compared to the four-cycle gasoline engine (Fig. 93). However, the popular General Motors marine diesels are two-cycle machines. Externally, they look quite like other engines but the internal works are different. Combustion air is not sucked in by the pistons, as on four-cycle diesels, it is blown in by a geared air blower (Fig. 4). Exhaust gases are not forced out by an upward stroke of the piston, they are blown out ahead of the fresh incoming air which is propelled by the mechanical blower.

There are exhaust valves in the cylinder head and inlet holes or ports in the cylinder walls near the bottom. The inlet ports are positioned as to be completely uncovered when the piston is down at bottom center.

The cycle starts with exhaust valves open, piston down at bottom and air ports uncovered. Fresh air blows in the ports, swirls up through the cylinder and out of the exhaust valves. Burned materials from the previous cycle are swept out by the gale of air, and the cylinder is left freshly charged. As the piston starts up, exhaust valves

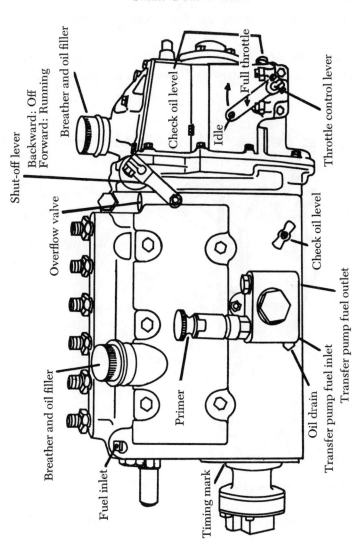

Fig. 92. *The Bosch fuel injection pump assembly.*

close, the piston covers the inlet ports and compression starts. The piston goes all the way up on compression, fuel injection occurs, then combustion and power stroke. When the piston is fairly well down on the power stroke,

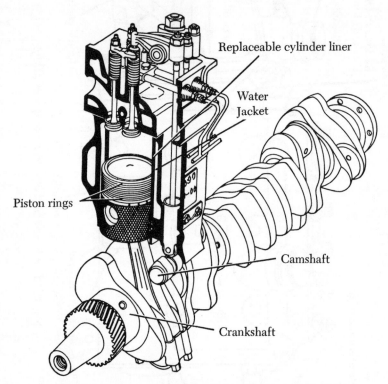

Fig. 93. *Cutaway view of a Cummins four-cycle diesel.*

the exhaust valves open, relieving pressure. Then the piston uncovers the air ports, air rushes in and the cycle repeats.

The two-cycle principle is nicely adapted to the diesel

because it is possible to use a mechanical blower and forcefully scavenge the cylinder with a gale of fresh air. This cannot be done on a gasoline two-cycle motor because the blower would be forcing burnable mixture through the cylinder and out the exhaust valve. It would be wasteful and dangerous. Notice, too, that there is no

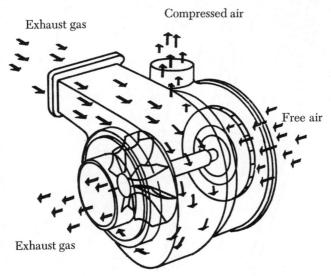

Fig. 94. *Cutaway view of a turbocharger used on a Cummins marine diesel.*

crankcase compression in a two-cycle diesel and no mixing of lubricating oil in the fuel.

Both two- and four-cycle diesels can be supercharged. Cummins, Caterpillar, G.M., Mercedes are among the manufacturers who supply supercharged marine diesels (Fig. 94).

A normal, unsupercharged diesel breathes naturally.

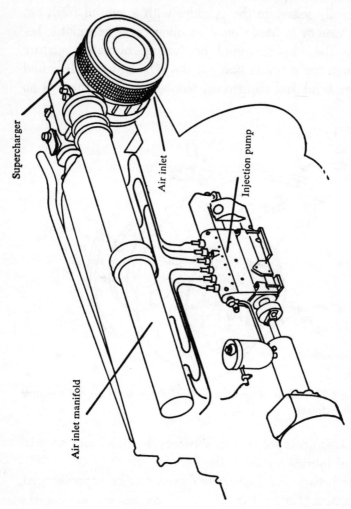

Supercharger

Air inlet

Injection pump

Air inlet manifold

Fig. 95. A Mercedes-Benz six cylinder diesel engine equipped with an exhaust gas powered supercharger.

That is, its pistons or blower suck in combustion air at atmospheric pressure. A supercharged diesel, however, is equipped with a high-speed air compressor which forces air into the diesel inlet under pressure, hence there is more air in the cylinders for combustion and the injectors can feed more fuel per revolution. Result: more power.

Some superchargers are driven by a train of gears from the crankshaft and some are driven by an exhaust turbine. The exhaust driven machines are called turbo-blowers or turbo-chargers.

The turbo-charger looks a little like a tank type vacuum cleaner (Fig. 95). Into one side roars hot diesel exhaust gas; the hot gas impinges on turbine buckets and makes the turbine spin and whine at tens of thousands of r.p.m. The turbine shaft has a centrifugal compressor impeller on the other end. The compressor sucks in outside air, compresses it and shoves it into the diesel's inlet manifold under pressure. It is a boot-strap operation: The spent exhaust gases, ordinarily thrown away, are forced to do the work of the compressing inlet air.

A supercharged diesel is smaller and lighter than a natural breathing one. For example, Cummins makes a marine diesel of 743 cubic inches piston displacement. The engine delivers 220 horespower naturally aspirated, 262 horsepower fitted with turbo-charger.

Chapter Fifteen

DIESEL INJECTION SYSTEMS

THE ENGINE that Rudolf Diesel built in 1897 had a complicated fuel injection system which utilized both fuel pump and air compressor. The early diesel engines had slow acting injection systems which blasted fuel into the cylinder along with a charge of compressed air. During early experiments, Dr. Diesel even operated his engine by blowing finely pulverized coal dust into the cylinder, using high pressure air injection. Original injection systems were crude and were the principal limiting factor to the diesel's speed.

For years engineers worked diligently to simplify and to refine the diesel's injection system, and by the mid-nineteen twenties the modern, high speed, liquid fuel injection system was coming into its own. It is this refined, accurate hydro-mechanical mechanism which makes possible the dynamic, fast spinning, marine diesel.

The diesel has no spark plugs or electrically timed ignition, but depends entirely upon the injection system to give precise timing to combustion. The diesel has no carburetor to meter fuel and mix with air, but depends upon the injection system to perform this function. Therefore, it is apparent that the injection components are called upon to perform the accurate operations of both ignition and carburetion. It is obvious, then, that the system must be constructed with the ultimate degree of precision. Watchmaker's precision goes into every injector component.

The very heart of every diesel injection system is a finely fitted, high pressure liquid fuel pump which receives low pressure fuel oil and immediately punches the pressure to thousands of pounds per square inch. The enormous surge of pressure injects fuel into the cylinder like the rush of an angry thunder cloud. The fuel oil, with several tons of kick behind it, bursts into the combustion space as a fine, violently tumbling mist which smashes head-on into the turbulent red-hot compressed air. The oil mist and compressed air combine in a searing hot flame which gives the diesel its might.

The exact time at which the pump piston or plunger rises on the pressure stroke is part of the engine timing sequence. In order to assure accuracy of timing, the pump plunger is driven by a cam carefully geared to the engine crankshaft. The pump piston or plunger is operated quite like an ordinary inlet or exhaust valve: A cam pushes the plunger on the working stroke and a powerful spring, like a valve spring, returns it to rest.

The Bosch pump consists of a housing having a camshaft and one cam for each pump, one plunger and cylinder for each diesel cylinder (Fig. 96). In the Bosch system, the pump plungers are provided with helical groove in the plunger wall and the plunger is rotatable while working. Fuel enters the cylinder through ports in the cylinder wall. A quantity of fuel injected by the plunger is varied by rotating the plunger on its axis. The pump might be compared to a strange, make-believe,

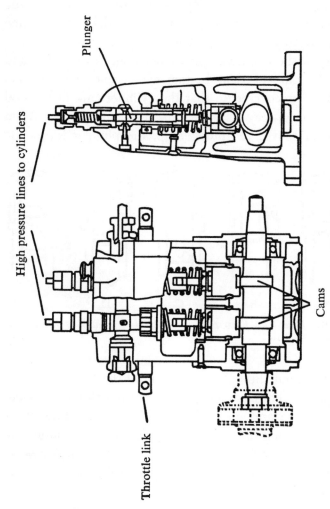

Fig. 96. *The Bosch injection pump assembly for a two cylinder diesel.*

two-cycle outboard motor in which throttling is accomplished by rotating a slope top piston. Changing the piston position rotationally would alter the effective time of uncovering the inlet ports in the cylinder wall.

Fig. 97 shows a Bosch pump in action. In views (a) and (c) the plunger is at bottom center and the two fuel ports are uncovered so that the cylinder can fill with oil from the gravity tank or low pressure pump. When the cam shoves the plunger up, the plunger forces the

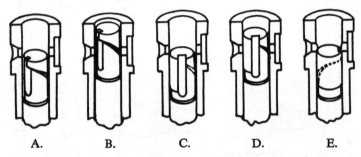

A.   B.   C.   D.   E.

Fig. 97. *How the flow rate is controlled in a Bosch injector pump.*

fuel back out through the ports until the top face blocks the ports. The remaining fuel is shot out through the delivery valve and injected into the cylinder. Fuel flows from the pump until the helical edge of the spiral groove uncovers the right hand port. This instantly relieves the pressure even though the plunger is still going up on the pressure stroke.

In the same figure view (b) shows the right port being uncovered by the spiral groove. In views (a) and (b) the throttle is wide open, in views (c) and (d) the throttle is half open, and in (e) the throttle is at "stop" and no fuel is injected at all.

In practice, the plungers are rotated by rack and pinion in conjunction with suitable linkage to the governor included in the injector pump assembly housing. For high power the plungers are rotated for maximum fuel delivery; for idle and low speed, the plungers are rotated in the opposite direction. The engine is stopped by rotating the plungers until the pressure relief grooves are in constant alignment with the fuel ports.

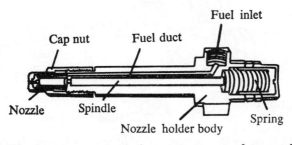

Fig. 98. *A cutaway view of an injector nozzle assembly.*

In the Bosch system, precise timing of injection is accomplished by precision manufacture of pump cams and the exact shape of the plungers and their helix-slot. Injection always starts at the instant the plunger crown covers the fuelports, and injection is finished when the groove uncovers the ports. Injection starts at the same time for all speeds but continues for a longer period as the throttle is advanced.

If the injection pump is the heart of the system, then surely the injection nozzle assembly is the nerve center (Fig. 98).

The injection nozzle is fitted into the diesel cylinder much like the spark plugs of the gasoline engine. The function of the nozzle assembly (Fig. 99) is to receive the precisely metered quantity of fuel from the injection pump, atomize it mechanically, and squirt it violently into the combustion chamber in definite, misty, spray pattern. Smooth engine performance depends upon good injection nozzles.

The nozzle assembly shown in Fig. 98 is from a Gray

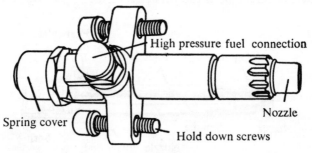

Fig. 99. *View of the nozzle assembly removed from the diesel's cylinder head.*

Marine diesel and is quite typical. Operation is simple: The metered quantity of fuel from the injection pump enters the holder through the inlet connection and passes through ducts to the pressure chamber just above the nozzle valve. At the split instant that fuel pressure acting on the valve exceeds 1,800 pounds, the powerful spring allows the valve to be lifted; then fuel squirts from the nozzle in an atomized flash. Fuel continues to hiss until the injection pump ceases delivery. Then a positive, instantaneous cut-off of fuel occurs as the valve is snapped into its seat by a powerful spring force. The positive action of the spring loaded valve eliminates dribbling of fuel into the cylinder after injection. Dribbling or drip from the nozzle would cause smoke, soot and fouling of cylinders.

A small amount of fuel seepage between lapped guide surfaces of nozzle and body is necessary for lubrication. This leakage accumulates around the spindle and in the spring compartment, then drains back to the tank through leak-off tubes. You may have noticed that most injector assemblies have two sets of tubes or small pipes attached: One set is the high pressure connection from the injector pump, the other is the low pressure leak-off.

The high pressure tubing or piping between injector pump and injector nozzle is not simple, ordinary, commercial copper tubing such as used for fuel transfer. It is special, steel, thick-wall tubing designed to handle tons of hydrostatic pressure. The high pressure tubes are a tailored part of the injection system, with exact diameter and length engineered to match the individual engine. The resilience of the tubing has a marked effect on engine timing. If incorrect lines are used between injection pumps and nozzles the engine may be mis-timed and suffer from nozzle dribble or fuel leakage.

Thus far we have discussed the Bosch system used on many marine engines including Gray and Mercedes-Benz, but other marine diesels use entirely different injection systems:

Cummins marine engines are fitted with a unique system designed and built by the Cummins people for their own engines (Figs. 100 and 101). They call it a pressure-time system because the metering of the exact fuel charge depends upon accurately governed pressure and precise interval of time, time being a function of engine speed. The system consists of four principal elements:

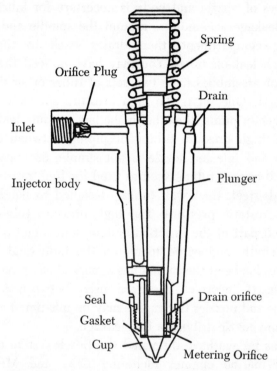

Fig. 100. *An Injector from a Cummins diesel.*

1. A gear pump to draw fuel from the fuel tank and deliver it to individual injectors for each cylinder.

2. Pressure regulator to control pressure of fuel fed to individual injector pumps.

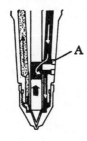

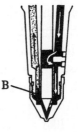

Metering

Start up-stroke

As the plunger moves up, the fuel supply hole A is uncovered. This allows fuel to circulate through the injector and out of the drain at the left. Most of the fuel is returned to the fuel tank.

Now the plunger has uncovered the metering orifice B , allowing fuel to enter the injector cup. The length of time opening is uncovered and pressure determines the quantity of fuel injected.

Injection complete

Injecting fuel

On downstroke, plunger "pushes" fuel through holes in the injector cup and into the cylinder as an exceptionally fine spray, insuring thorough mixing with the air and complete burning.

Following injection the plunger remains seated until it is time for it to repeat its cycle. The action of the injector plunger is controlled by the engine camshaft assuring injection at most effective time.

Fig. 101. *How the Cummins P. T. injection system works.*

3. Fuel passages of exact size and type so that fuel is distributed to all injectors with equal pressure at all speeds and loads.

4. Injectors to receive low pressure fuel from the gear

pump and deliver it to individual combustion chambers at the right time.

The injectors on a Cummins diesel incorporate the high pressure injection pump, the pump being actuated by push rod and rocker arm from the engine camshaft. From above the engine head the mechanism looks almost exactly like a valve spring and tappet.

The four views of Fig. 93 show the Cummins injector in action.

General Motors Marine Diesels use an injection system somewhat like Cummins, but there are important differences:

General Motors uses unit injectors which are combination injection nozzle and high pressure pump actuated by push rod and rocker arm from engine camshaft. Precise timing is obtained from camshaft rotation and timing adjustment is made by set screw and lock nut, as on an exhaust valve (Fig. 102). The injectors are fed with fuel oil at about sixty pounds per square inch, pressure being supplied by gear pump, as on Cummins units. However, the great difference between Cummins and General Motors is that while Cummins controls the low pressure flow accurately as means of metering fuel to the injector, General Motors does not; it simply pumps an adequate flow of fuel to the unit injector; accurate control of injection quantity is controlled right in the injector by mechanical rack and helical groove in the plunger (Fig. 103).

The Roosa-Master injection pump is used by Gray on some of their marine diesels and it looks amazingly like an ignition distributor from a gas engine. As a matter of fact it is a distributor, a hydraulic one, not electrical (Fig. 104).

The Roosa-Master unit combines a low pressure transfer pump, high pressure injection pump, metering valve and fuel distributor all in one compact housing. Its workings are quite different from other injection systems:

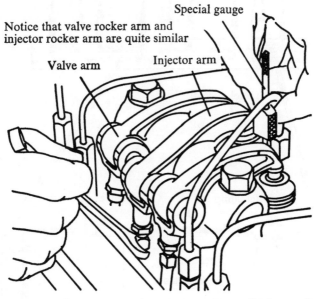

Fig. 102. *Timing the fuel injectors for a General Motors diesel.*

The unit has just one single cylinder, opposed plunger, inlet-metering high pressure pump to serve all the cylinders of the engine. The injection pump has a single cylinder containing two little plungers or pistons which oppose each other and slide in and out of the cylinder as the pump rotates. The plungers are actuated through rollers by a stationary, internal cam ring. Fuel is metered to the cylinder, the pistons are forced together by the cam ring, and fuel is ejected from the cylinder under great pressure at the exact time that drilled passages are in align-

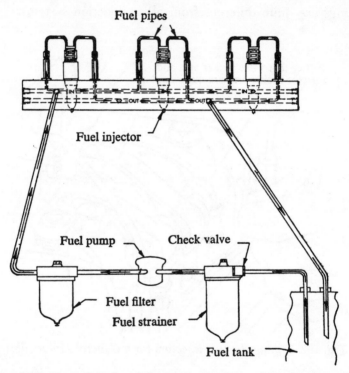

Fig. 103. *Typical fuel supply system of General Motors Series-71 diesel.*

ment from the cylinder, through the distributor and to the injector nozzle tubing.

Most injection systems are equipped with several accessories, perhaps the most important being a series of

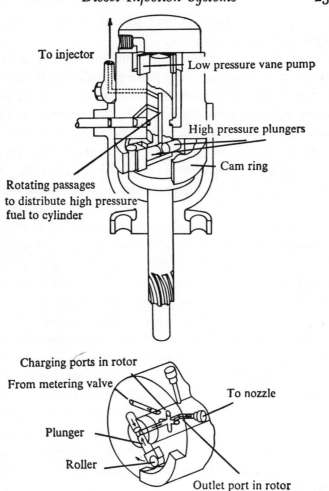

Fig. 104. *Sectional schematic views of a Roosa-Master pump.*

fuel filters and strainers. Dirt and dust are death to an injection pump or injection nozzle valve; consequently, diesel engines are equipped with primary and secondary filter in series. Some injection systems even have a third, very fine ceramic filter placed in the circuit just prior to the injection plunger.

Another accessory found on all marine diesels is a speed governor. The Bosch pump has a governor built into one end of the housing, the injector control racks being positioned in response to the governor, the governor, in turn, being controlled by a throttle. The Roosa-Master has a built-in centrifugal governor. General Motors diesels have a governor separate from the injectors, but the governor controls all the injectors through the enclosed linkage.

Now, then, a brief review of the diesel injection system:

Fuel, similar to domestic burner oil, is sucked from the storage tank by a transfer pump, filtered clean, and supplied under modest pressure to the injection pumps. Plungers of the injection pumps ram the pressure up to thousands of pounds per square inch, and force the oil to the nozzle assemblies in each diesel cylinder. The nozzles have heavily loaded check valves which open under high pressure and allow the oil to hiss into the combustion chamber, intermix with red hot air and burst into tornado-like flame. Some systems have injection pumps remote from the engine cylinders (like Gray and Mercedes-Benz) and some have injector plunger combined with nozzle assembly (like Cummins and General Motors.)

What owner maintenance is required to keep the injection system in sound condition? There is one prime thing: Keep the fuel clean and service the fuel filters regularly. Other than that, unless special tools and fixtures are available, it is best to leave the injection system alone.

Opening it up to putter or to tinker invites trouble due to dirt sneaking into the delicate works. Dirt is the arch enemy of injectors.

The scope of owner maintenance varies greatly from one engine to another; the prime guide is the engine maintenance manual. On some engines there are straightforward operations such as bleeding of lines, balancing of injectors, checking timing or measuring fuel return flow on low pressure lines. On most engines it is not too hard to change an injector, should that be necessary. But in most cases, unless emergency measures are required, it is best to leave the injection system buttoned up safe from grit and grime.

Chapter Sixteen

OPERATING A MARINE DIESEL EFFICIENTLY

PICTURE a forty-footer with flying bridge and tall out-riggers heading proudly through the inlet chop. She pitches gently into the rolling swells and skims sheets of white spray abeam. As she rolls past and shows her transom, the rumble of exhaust is rhythmic; wisps of steam curl aft and evaporate from the bumbling pipes. Here is smooth, deep power—no smoke, no smell, no fuss. This is the diesel yacht in action. This is the diesel at its best.

It is easy to keep a marine diesel in the pink because the machine is sturdily built to tough commercial specifications. Marine diesels are precision built of rugged metals; they are operated, tested and adjusted at the factory. The manufacturer does his best to deliver a fine engine; it is up to the owner to keep it in fettle.

A new diesel should be broken in carefully because the first fifty hours of use have a significant bearing on the engine's longevity. The following break-in recommendations taken from the Cummins H Series Diesel Guide are applicable to all diesels:

1. Operate most of the time at one-half to three-quarters throttle. Do not operate at maximum horsepower for more than five minutes at a time.

2. Do not idle engine for long periods because this will cause the cylinder walls to glaze before the piston rings seat properly, and the engine will continue to use too much lubricating oil.

3. Keep a close watch on instruments. Back off on throttle if oil temperature reaches 200°F. or if water temperature exceeds 185°F.

It is smart to keep a watchful eye on the oil pressure

Fig. 105. *Using a torque wrench to tighten cylinder head nuts.*

gauge during the break-in period. Most diesel manufacturers recommend that the crankcase oil and oil filter be changed after the first 50 to 100 hours' operation (Fig. 105). On most diesels it is recommended that the cylinder head nuts be re-tightened after the first 50 hours, and valve clearances should be adjusted at the same time (Fig. 106).

Complete the valve adjusting after tightening the cylinder head nuts, because tightening the head may alter valve clearance slightly. The head nuts should be tightened with a torque wrench to the recommended tightness, and the valves adjusted to the specified clearance with the engine either hot or cold as definitely called for in the manual. The engine manual is a valuable tool. It

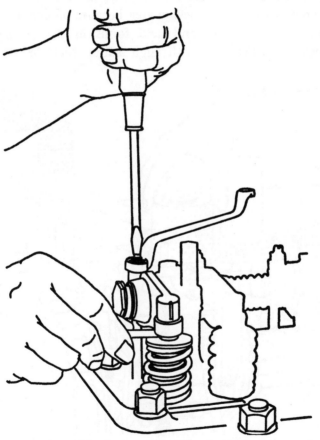

Fig. 106. *Adjusting valve tappets. This should be done following engine break-in.*

gives specific procedures for break-in and adjustment. Follow the instructions carefully; you will be well repaid.

Throughout the diesel's life, one of the important service procedures will be the regular crankcase oil changes. Oil changes are important. They are more important to the diesel than to the gas engine because oil contamination is more severe and acid forms in the oil more quickly, particularly with high sulfur fuel. When in

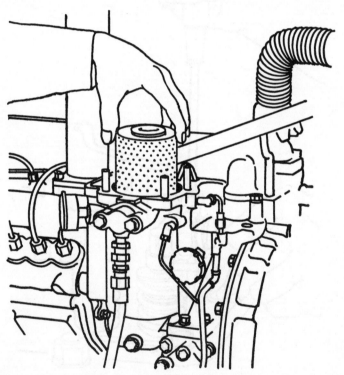

Fig. 107. *Changing the fuel filter element on a Caterpillar diesel. Clean fuel is important to all diesels.*

doubt, change oil more frequently, and always do it when the engine is warm. The best time is immediately after a good run, when the oil is all churned up and the foreign matter is suspended. Use exactly the oil recommended for your specific engine.

The lube oil filter element should be changed several times each season or about once every 200 hours.

Some engines, like the Mercedes-Benz, have injection pumps in a housing which looks almost like a miniature inline engine with tiny crankcase. These units have a dip stick and drain plug, just like an engine, and the lubricating oil should be changed in the pump housing at the gine in fine condition does well to set up some sort of preventive maintenance schedule. This schedule will vary from one engine to another, naturally, but basically the pattern will be similar.

Gray marine has a suggested maintenance schedule for their little four-cylinder, light-weight diesel. It can be applied to almost any four-cycle diesel with minor modifications. Here it is in a nutshell:

Daily
Check water in cooling system (Fresh water cooling).
Check lube oil in crankcase.
Check lube oil in transmission.
One turn of grease cup on sea water pump.
Overall visual inspection of engine.

Once A Week
Test electrolite level in battery. It is important to keep
  battery fully charged during cold weather.
Look for water in fuel oil filters; drain if necessary.

Every 100 Hours

Change oil in crankcase. Use symbol 9250 oil, SAE 30.

Replace cartridge in lube oil filter.

Clean air intake screen.

Test tension of "V" belts.

Inspect engine for loose bolts, nuts, leaks.

Examine sea-water pump for leaks at packing gland.

Put a few drops of engine oil in hinge cap oilers on generator. There is an oil cup at each end.

Every 200 Hours

Change transmission oil. Use engine oil, symbol 9250, SAE 30.

Repeat all 100 hour operations.

Gauge valve clearances—0.014" hot.

Check ignition timing—21°B.T.D.C.

Tighten cylinder head nuts: Torque 100 to 110 foot-pounds.

Wash element of primary fuel filter.

Replace element in fuel oil second filter.

Inspect crankcase and transmission breathers: Wash if necessary.

Put two or three drops (no more!) engine oil in wick under oil plug at right end of cranking motor. Caution: Excess oil will foul brushes and commutator.

Clean exterior of engine.

Every 1000 Hours

Repeat all 100 and 200 hour maintenance operations.

Clean and check injector nozzles.

Clean energy cells.

Prepack sea-water pump.

Inspect starter and generator brushes, commutator and
bearings. Replace or overhaul if necessary.

Every 2000 Hours

Repeat all the previous operations for 100, 200, and 1000
hours. Remove cylinder head and grind valves. Install new piston rings. Inspect cylinder liners. Check
bearings and valve guides. Carefully examine entire
engine. After reassembly, test compression pressure:
Desirable pressure is 300 to 325 pounds at cranking
speed, all cylinders with uniform readings.

The Cummins Diesel people have printed a little book-
let entitled "Ten Maintenance Steps." The remarks in the
book are straight to the point and apply to all diesels.
The Cummins ten points are:

1. Keep dirt out of the engine. Dirt is the cause of
most engine wear. Much of it is gritty material ranging
from less than 0.0001 inch diameter to coarse sand. The
particles are hard enough to penetrate the toughest oil
film and grind away metal. You can easily illustrate the
abrasive effects of dirt: Mix a small pinch of soil with
lubricating oil and put it between two sheets of glass.
Exert a little pressure and rub the slides of glass together.
Wash off the dirt and look at the scratches. Think what
this does to the engine's inside. Save dollars by keeping
out dirt (Fig. 107).

2. Maintain a lubricating film on all bearing surfaces.
Use quality oils, watch the dip stick, change oil frequently
and watch oil pressure gauge. Consider this: Down time

and overhaul expense for one engine failure may cost as much as 1,000 oil changes.

3. Regulate the engine's fuel. Use fuel which burns readily and completely. Buy fuel which is clean and to correct specification. Know that the injection system is properly adjusted to deliver the right quantity of fuel at the right time. Poor fuel or too much fuel causes black smoke, lube oil dilution and damage to turbochargers. Dirty fuel may wreck the injectors.

4. Control operating temperatures. Diesel combustion temperatures are high enough to melt the engine. Complete failure of the cooling system will ruin the engine in a few minutes. Watch the temperature and control it so that it stays between 160°F. and 190°F. When coolant temperature is below 160°F. fuel may not burn readily or produce full power. However, when water temperature exceeds 190°F. and the engine is operating under full load, the lubricating oil may get so hot and thin that it will not lubricate effectively.

5. Guard against corrosion. Many engine owners have been shocked to find water in the crankcase and to learn that it got there through pinholes or wormholes that started on the water side of the cylinder liners. Often the damage progresses to the point that liners and block have to be replaced. This eating away of metal is likely to occur in any cooling system where the coolant is not treated to prevent the action. There are many causes of corrosion, including acid, salt or air in the coolant. Corrosion can be controlled by the use of magnesium waste plates and the installation of a chemical corrosion resistor.

6. Let the engine breathe. A diesel requires about

12,500 gallons of air for every gallon of fuel consumed. The engine must breathe freely; intake and exhaust must not be restricted by dirty air cleaner, damaged silencer or piping of inadequate size. The amount of power which can be developed is as dependent upon air as upon fuel. If there is too little air, excess fuel will cause smoky exhaust (Fig. 108).

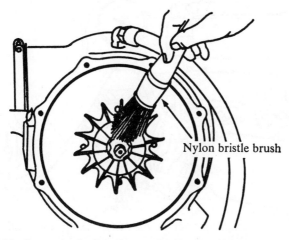

Nylon bristle brush

Fig. 108. *Routine cleaning of turbocharger compressor wheel on a Cummins diesel.*

7. Prevent overspeeding. Most diesels are protected against overspeeding by factory set governors. Do not invite engine failure by tampering with the governor. A diesel not governor-equipped should be loaded with a large enough propeller to prevent overspeeding.

8. Know your engine's condition. Watch the exhaust, the temperature, the oil pressure gauge.

9. Correct troubles while they are simple. Preventive

maintenance is a series of simple check, replacement and repair operations intended to forestall progressive damage. Delaying a maintenance job that needs doing is a reckless gamble (Fig. 109).

10. Schedule and control your maintenance. Keep track of the dates and engine hours when the engine was

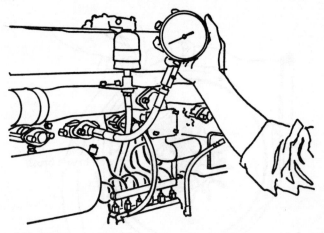

Fig. 109. *Testing cylinder compression using a special gauge hooked into the injector nozzle opening.*

serviced or repaired. A neat engine logbook helps keep an accurate record.

Routine maintenance of the General Motors two-cycle marine diesel closely follows the pattern of other engines except that the scavenging air blower and air box are included in the schedule (Fig. 110).

On General Motors diesels, the rotary blower screen is cleaned every 1,000 hours. The air box has small water drains to drip off condensed moisture from the air blower, and these drain tubes should be inspected and cleaned every 500 hours.

The Lister air-cooled marine diesel and the American Marc air-cooled diesel have no water jackets or cooling

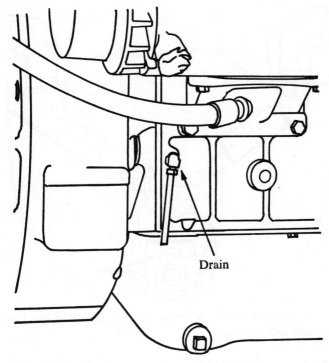

Drain

Fig. 110. *Air box drain on a General Motors diesel should be checked every 500 hours.*

water pumps to service. However, the fins on the cylinder, the injector body and the head need routine cleaning every several hundred hours, and the vanes in the air blower require occasional cleaning.

Installation of the Lister and American Marc diesels is critical because they must be supplied with unlimited fresh, cool outside air lest they roast to death. Separate inlet and outlet air ducts must be provided so that hot

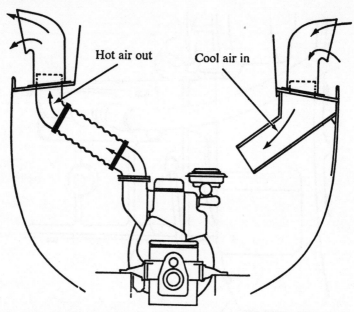

Fig. 111. *Correct air ducts assure proper cooling of the Lister air-cooled marine diesel.*

cooling air does not re-circulate in the engine compartment (Fig. 111).

Incidentally, these tiny diesels, fitted with geared hand crank (Fig. 112), are just about the most simple, gadget-free power available. There is no ignition system, battery, starter, generator or wiring to fret about. Nothing but pure, simple diesel. Of course, these engines can be supplied with an electric starter, but the simplicity of the geared hand crank is surely attractive, particularly for auxiliary power.

Intelligent diesel operation and the observance of a few rules can contribute many scores of hours to the engine's life.

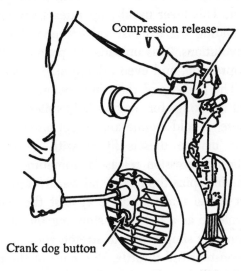

Fig. 112. *The geared hand crank on the American Marc single cylinder diesel.*

Marine diesels are like marine gas engines in that they should be warmed easily before being pushed hard. Start the engine, then put it under light load and easy throttle until it has warmed; then it is ready for hard work. However, it is bad to warm the diesel by idling for a long time, because prolonged idling fouls the engine and may dilute the crankcase oil with unburned fuel.

Stopping the diesel properly is warm-up in reverse. If the engine has been working hard, throttle back and run at half speed or less for about five minutes before cutting the fuel. An easy run prior to shut-down allows the temperatures within the engine to equalize before the moving parts become still.

Many marine diesels are fitted with a compression release lever. This lever usually operates a simple mechanism for holding the exhaust valves open throughout all engine revolutions. This unloads the pistons so that there is no compression, and even a large engine can be hand-cranked. The purpose of the compression release is to allow hand-cranking for engine adjustment or to help "break-loose" a cold engine and to get oil circulating. On Caterpillar marine diesels fitted with gasoline engine starter, the compression release is sometimes used while the gas engine spins the diesel and warms it prior to starting. Most diesel makers advise against the use of compression release as a means of stopping the engine.

An ultimately simple way to stretch your diesel's life is to avoid constant full throttle. Run most of the time at 85 per cent of full r.p.m. or less. It is an economical thing to do.

Chapter Seventeen

ELIMINATING NOISE AND VIBRATION

THE MARINE ENGINE is a noisy monster by nature. It could not be otherwise. How can a machine be inherently quiet when its insides are racked by thousands of explosions a minute, its intake is sucking up a tornado of swirling, whistling air and the exhaust is belching a hurricane of boiling, searing gases. Then, as if the violent thermal activity were not enough, the poor animal is plagued by dozens of parts flying up and down, spinning around and clattering back and forth. Not a tranquil picture.

Outboard or inboard, gasoline or diesel, the marine engine is born a loud, lusty creature which must be hushed before being fit company.

Years ago, when cars had cut-outs and outboard motors had open stacks, it was considered quite sporty to have a staccato, explosive exhaust. "Wow!" they thought, "listen to that fierce power." But even then, the impressed, if deafened, listener was wrong. What he really should have thought was, "Wow! Listen to that horrible racket." There is little connection between offensive noise and useful power.

Today, a nerve-shattering exhaust roar is looked upon as high school stuff; in fact, in many localities open exhausts are illegal. With the boat population increasing greatly, noise reduction becomes more important. Imagine a crowded harbor on a Saturday afternoon if all the boats had open exhaust stacks. Atomic war would be quieter.

The outboard motor people have done a wonderful job of hushing their product. Modern outboards are quiet. The carefully engineered underwater exhausts reduce that noise to a comfortable bumble, and the rubber mounts plus vibration insulators cut hull vibration to a low level. Shrouds and hoods are placed over the spinning machinery and accessory drives so that air-borne noise is soaked up. Propellers are rubber shock mounted so that tremors from that source are blocked from hull and passengers. The result of careful noise reduction engineered into the outboard motor is that its users enjoy a quiet, comfortable boat while the neighbors enjoy peace and quiet.

Inboard engine manufacturers have a tougher problem. They build only the engine; the user must silence the machine.

But the inboard engine makers have done a lot to make their motors quieter, too. Inboards are better balanced than formerly; this contributes to reduced hull vibration. Inboards are furnished with rubber mounts to insulate engine vibration from the balance of the craft. Gears and accessory drives are quieter now.

Many stock boat builders pay close attention to making their craft quiet. Engines are shock mounted, exhausts are hushed, hull and superstructure are insulated with sound absorbing material. These are the measures taken to make a boat quiet and livable.

If your boat is too noisy for comfortable cruising, instigate a silencing campaign. Concentrate on getting rid of two kinds of noise which frays nerves: These are air-borne noise and hull-borne buzzing. Hull noise is that chatter-

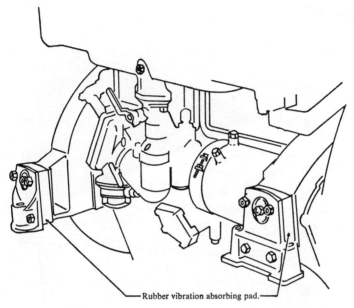

Rubber vibration absorbing pad.

Fig. 113. *Rubber mounts prevent engine vibration from being transmitted to the hull.*

ing vibration which sets up standing waves in bilge water and moves glasses across the table.

Give first attention to the loudest air-borne noise, the exhaust din. There are four easy ways to reduce the roar:

1. Install one or more silencers.
2. Dump cooling water into the exhaust gas.
3. Use the flexible steam hose for the exhaust pipe.

4. Install an elbow or deflector on the end of the exhaust pipe.

A marine exhaust silencer does the same thing for your boat's engine as the muffler does for your car. It softens the staccato. "But," you ask, "does it also reduce engine power?"

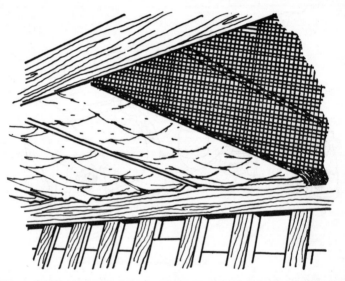

Fig. 114. *Overhead of an engine compartment being padded with sound absorbing material. Soft matting is held in place with metal screening.*

A properly installed silencer of correct design and dimensions adds so little back pressure to the exhaust that the change in power is negligible. Even at full throttle on the largest engines, power loss is tiny, provided, of course, that the proper size silencer is used. It is easy to select the correct silencer: There are several types and

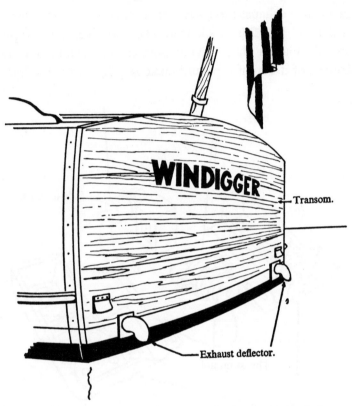

Fig. 115. *A right angle deflector on the bitter end of the exhaust pipe directs the exhaust blast downward and keeps the engine quiet.*

makes on the marine market. If you write to the silencer manufacturers, tell them the make and model of your engine and they will recommend the right muffler. In most cases the silencer size is defined by the pipe or tubing size which it fits.

For most installations, if your engine is fitted with a

given size exhaust pipe, say 2-inch, then the right silencer is defined as a 2-inch silencer. The manufacturers supply an information sheet giving pointers on installation. Silencers of different type and make require vertical or hori-

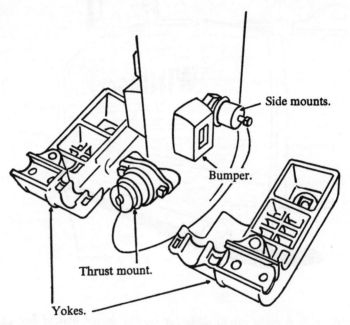

Fig. 116. *These shock mounts and bumpers isolate vibration on the lower unit of an outboard motor.*

zontal mounting as specified, and some must be facing so that "inlet" and "outlet" connections are not reversed.

Most silencers are "wet" type and depend upon a flow of water along with the exhaust gas. The efficiency of many silencers depends upon a good flow of water for noise reduction and cooling. In most installations water volume is sufficient if all the engine cooling water is poured into the exhaust. If the engine is cooled by fresh water using a closed system and keel cooler, then a separate raw water pump must be provided to cool the exhaust pipe and provide water flow through the silencer.

Some auxiliary sailboats have engines located deep below the water line. Cooling water cannot be pumped into the exhaust line close to the engine because water will not run uphill, it would drain back to the exhaust manifold and wreck the engine. Special silencers are made for installation where the engine is below the water line; the silencer, incorporating a special water trap, is located well above the water level. The exhaust pipe between the engine and the silencer is either "dry" or is water-jacketed and cooling water is piped directly to the silencer, then flows out the tail pipe together with the exhaust gas.

A dry exhaust system utilizing dry silencer or heavy-duty muffler is all right; many work boats are rigged this way and the exhaust goes up a stack. But there is a heat problem. An exhaust system carrying no water runs almost red hot and requires careful lagging both to prevent fire and to protect crew members from being seared.

Where the ultimate in quiet is desired, two silencers may be placed in series. We saw this done last season on a Chrysler Ace and the results were excellent. The Ace was fitted with two Model MO, 3-inch Maxim Silencers in series; the exhaust roar was reduced to a murmur and the loss in top engine r.p.m. was unreadable on an accurate tachometer.

The best arrangement on V-8 engines is one silencer for each cylinder bank. When the installation is made, be sure that each side gets approximately the same quantity of cooling water.

Wet exhaust allows the use of a steam hose for the exhaust pipe and the pliant hose quiets the exhaust a little. Metal pipe is resilient; it rings and adds to the exhaust noise. Steam hose is pliable, soft and will not am-

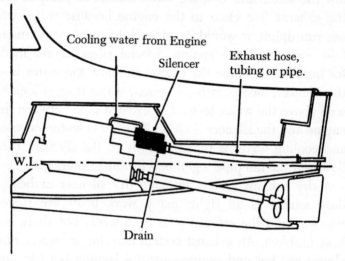

Cooling water from Engine

Silencer

Exhaust hose, tubing or pipe.

W.L.

Drain

Fig. 117. *Exhaust silencer installed on a powerboat with an engine installed above the waterline.*

plify the cyclic exhaust clatter. In addition, metal pipe or tube transmits engine vibration to the hull; steam hose does not.

A right angle deflector or elbow at the bitter end of the exhaust pipe shoots the noise and fuss downward toward the water and helps reduce exhaust roar. A deflector seems to be particularly effective used in cooperation with a silencer. A presentable deflector can be made from round 3-inch copper downspout material. Buy a 90° copper down-spout elbow, shape it to suit with hacksaw, then clamp it to the end of the exhaust pipe with a good stainless steel hose clamp.

When you have stifled the exhaust racket, turn your

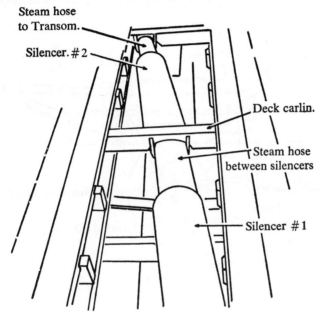

Fig. 118. *The ultimate in exhaust noise squelching. Two Monel metal silencers installed below-deck on the exhaust line.*

attention to other air-borne engine noises. After the exhaust is quieted, some of the other noises will become more apparent. A boat has numerous large surfaces which are resilient and which bounce noise around to make it more annoying. One phase of your silencing program is to pad and insulate some of the surfaces with sound absorbent material. You know how much more hushed a living room is with rugs, drapes and cushions; remove these flaccid things and the room booms with echoes. Your boat is the same. Cover some of the surfaces with soft, dead material and the noise will be squelched.

Prime noise reduction results when you line the engine

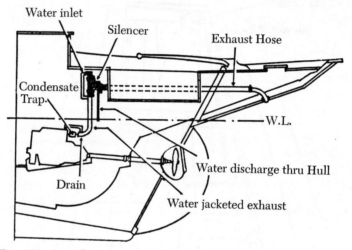

Fig. 119. *Installation of an exhaust silencer when the engine is located below the waterline.*

compartment and hatch cover with sound absorbent material. Cover all surfaces possible, but remember not to suffocate the engine. The cabin top frequently sounds like an overgrown kettledrum; pad it well. Many power boats have a large, flat wood panel inside the transom; pad this, too. The boat's sides, particularly in the engine region, may bounce noise back and forth. Padding between the frames will soften the echoes.

The propellers on twin-screw power boats are usually located under a fairly flat section of the hull bottom. As the propellers spin they bounce water shock waves off the hull and cause vibration. Also, of course, propeller vibration is transmitted to the hull through the struts attached to the bottom. This rumbling can be softened by padding the after part of hull and bilges with a dead material like foam rubber tucked down between the frames.

But watch out for rot. Bilge water will make a soggy mess of the insulating material and the warm mass will invite fungus spores to start their miserable work. Before installing the padding, swab the area with good marine anti-rot compound, then put the padding in so that removal is easy. Take the material out several times a year; dry it and give the hull another dose of copper naphthenate.

All boats are damp, soggy machines in some weather. Warm dampness and restricted ventilation invite mildew and rot. It pays to apply wood preservative to any area before installing sound absorbent pads or panels.

Engine noises are not only transmitted through the air, but also through engine bed, hull and superstructure. In fact, as the air noise is reduced and muffled, the buzzing vibration becomes more apparent. The basic way to reduce hull-transmitted vibration is to insulate the engine; float it on a cushion so that it keeps vibration to itself.

Rubber marine engine mounts are the most important step in blocking vibration. These mounts consist of engine bracket and mounting feet, the two halves of the mount being insulated from each other by a pad of rubber or neoprene. A marine engine mounted on such special brackets is floated from the engine bed and stringers; high-frequency vibration does not pass through the rubber and the engine seems quieter. The effect is demonstrated by a poorly balanced electric fan on a hardwood table. The fan will buzz and rattle; it will walk around the hardwood. But simply place it on a soft rubber mat and it quiets immediately. (It seems to. The fan is still noisy but the hard wood no longer amplifies the buzzing.)

Placing a marine engine on rubber mounts does not finish the job; vibration can still be telegraphed to the hull through the controls, instrument connections, exhaust system, fuel lines and propeller shaft. To do a good, Bristol-fashion job, all these attachments should be insulated.

Insulating the exhaust pipe is most important and also simple. At some section of the pipe before it reaches a solid hull clamp it must have a section of rubber steam hose to block vibration. If the entire length of the exhaust line is hose, so much the better.

If the installation uses "dry" exhaust, steam hose is out of the question. The best thing is a section of flexible metal hose and vibration-insulated clamps or hangers to carry the exhaust line. A "dry" exhaust line must be insulated for heat as well as noise. You can borrow a few ideas from Detroit. Examine the underpinnings of a modern car. The hot exhaust pipes and muffler are completely floated or insulated from the car frame. There is a complete sound barrier. The pipe hangers and brackets terminate at flexible mounts; they never touch the frame.

There are several ways to reduce vibration transmitted to the hull through the propeller shaft. The use of cutless rubber bushings at stern and strut bearings floats the shaft and blocks vibration effectively. Rubber bearings not

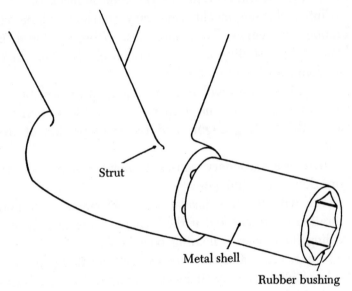

Strut

Metal shell

Rubber bushing

Fig. 120. *A Goodyear Cutless bearing being pressed into a propeller shaft strut mounting.*

only isolate engine vibration from the hull, but also block propeller vibration. Remember, though, that any stern or strut bearing, even the rubber ones, can contribute a little vibration and noise of their own if allowed to become loose and sloppy. Grab the propeller shaft at the propeller end and shake it hard; if the shaft rattles around willingly it is time to replace the bushings.

An insulated shaft coupling at the engine drive effectively isolates vibration from the propeller shaft and will also soak up a minor amount of shaft misalignment. There are couplings on the market in which the two flanges are insulated from each other by neoprene so that torque is transmitted but vibration is blocked.

Clutch shifting mechanisms may transmit engine vibration to remote boat locations. Vibration here is blocked by installing a rubber-bushed clevis where linkage connects to the clutch lever.

A rigid fuel line will not only telegraph noise, but is dangerous. The fuel line must have a flexible section between the floating engine and the rigid portion of the boat.

There are secondary causes of noise which you can hunt down and eliminate:

Even with the best insulation, some engine noise and vibration is present and if the boat has loose door hooks, rattling floor boards, floating boat hooks and such, they will buzz, rattle and fray nerves. Tighten things up and tie loose gear securely. Inspect steering linkage for buzzing and rattling; it is a common offender. Have propellers straightened and balanced regularly; a slightly off-beat propeller can make a terrible fuss. Test alignment of engine and propeller shaft; even a little mis-alignment can cause thumping and rumble.

Obviously, engine selection and operation can affect the noise level of your boat. The easier your hand on the throttle, the lower the roar.

Diesel engines have somewhat softer exhaust noise than gasoline; but the mechanical click-clack is sharper.

Low speed engines, gas or diesel, are easier on nerves than high speed ones. Slow engines may be just as loud when measured by instrument, but the lower pitch frays nerves less than the scream of a fast spinning mill. It is easy to crawl in and nurse a big machine revolving a thousand r.p.m., but nerve wracking to plaster your ear close to flying pistons at thirty-eight hundred. Likewise, on a long cruise, crewmen learn to hate each other less when the engine is clunking, not screaming.

Chapter Eighteen

MARINE TRANSMISSION AND GEARS

IT IS a pleasure to stand at a dockside and watch a careful yachtsman ease his power boat into a slip. He approaches slowly, maneuvers the boat with clutch and rudder, applies a little power when necessary and places the craft just where he wants her. No panic, no yelling, no excitement.

During the docking operation, the engine bumbles along at relatively constant speed, but the propeller must alternately push the boat forward, remain still, then pull the boat aft. It is the function of the marine transmission to provide forward, neutral and reverse to propeller-shaft rotation to make the changes smoothly, quickly. The marine transmission functions somewhat like an automatic automobile transmission but the marine unit must shift direction before the boat or propeller have come to rest.

Many marine transmissions incorporate reduction gears which reduce propeller shaft speed below engine revolutions. Reduction gearing is desirable in most boats which have high speed engines; the ratio is commonly in the 2:1 area. The reduction gears operate all the time, whether transmission is in forward or reverse. When the automobile transmission is in "high gear" or direct drive, the differential provides constant reduction gearing between engine and wheels, the ratio being roughly 3½:1 in a modern passenger car.

In a manually shifted automobile transmission, the clutch and gears are operated separately, the clutch being disengaged by foot pedal and the gears changed by hand lever. The marine transmission is different: the clutch and gears are interconnected and operated by one lever, generally referred to by marine folk as "the clutch."

Most marine transmissions consist of a gear set and two clutches, one clutch for forward, another for reverse. The two clutches may both be disc, or one may be disc and the other a band, or one a cone clutch and the other a band. Sometimes both are disc. There are many combinations.

Here is what happens in a typical marine transmission:

When the controls are in forward position, the reverse gears are de-clutched and removed from the power train by having the reverse clutch in neutral. At the same time, the forward clutch is tightly engaged so that power is transmitted straight through from the engine flywheel to the propeller shaft or reduction unit. When operating forward, power is transmitted directly through the forward clutch and no gears are operating in the power train.

When the control is moved to neutral, both clutches are disengaged and the transmission cannot transmit engine torque. Sometimes when the control is neutral, the propeller shaft will sneak around slowly either forward or reverse. This is due to a little clutch drag and is particularly noticeable when lubricating oil is cold and viscous.

Reverse is accomplished when the forward clutch is neutral and the reverse clutch engaged. The reverse clutch switches a gear cluster into the power path and reverses propeller-shaft rotation. The reverse gearing may be spur, helical, bevel or a planetary train of gears, depending on design details. In any event, the gears remain in constant mesh; shifting is done by manipulating the clutches, not by engaging the gears. In this regard, the marine transmission closely resembles automatic automobile transmissions which "shift" through clutches or bands. Here again control is by friction clutch activity, not by disengaging gears or rearranging a gear train.

Let us look into The Paragon Model SA2-120 marine transmission for details of typical transmission operation (Fig. 121):

The reverse gear assembly consists of a drum which serves both as gear case and clutch. Inside the gear case are three short pinion gears which mesh with the engine gear on the input shaft. These short pinions also mesh with three long pinions; the latter, in turn, mesh with a central gear supported on the bearings. This central gear is the propeller gear. It drives the propeller shaft.

Inside the drum, on center, is a multiple disc clutch. This clutch is engaged by pressure plate and toggle mechanism with linkage to the control shaft. The disc clutch gives forward drive.

Outside the planetary gear case (the drum) is a brake band which can frictionally grip the drum. This is the reverse clutch.

Operation in forward: Forward drive is obtained by

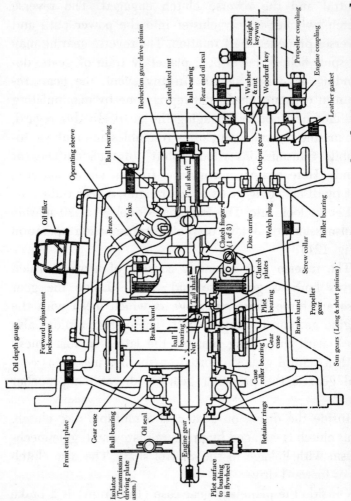

Fig. 121. Cross section of the Paragon transmission with reduction gears mounted at the output end.

locking the disc clutch. Locking is accomplished by the pressure of clutch fingers when the operating lever is thrown to forward position. When the discs are compressed, the entire reverse gear train is locked together as a solid, massive coupling. Since none of the inner gears can rotate in mesh, the gear case (drum) spins as a solid coupling; the gears remain motionless in their relationship to each other; engine rotation is transmitted directly to the tailshaft.

Operation in reverse: When the operating lever is thrown into reverse, the brake band is clamped tightly around the outside of the round gear case. Friction prevents the case from spinning. At the same instant that brake is applied to the drum, pressure on the multiple disc clutch is released; this disconnects the tailshaft from the gear case. Now the pinions inside the gear case are free to rotate, and the planetary gear train reverses the direction of the output shaft rotation.

Operation in neutral: In neutral position, both the disc clutch and brake band are free. No torque can be transmitted.

There are many different designs of planetary marine transmission. For example, Palmer built many gear boxes using two disc clutches rather than one disc clutch and one reverse band. With an eye to increasing friction area during reverse and to minimize reverse band wear, Palmer used a large plate clutch all the way around the planetary drum, sort of like the rings of Saturn.

Snow-Nabstedt retains the reverse band but substitutes a cone clutch in place of disc for forward drive. They do this because for equal size and weight a cone clutch can transmit more torque than plates.

The Capitol transmission incorporates still another variation of design: Wet disc clutch is used for forward and brake band for reverse, but in place of straight gears and pinions, the reverse gear cluster uses bevel gears, as in an automobile differential. This design is efficient and gives 100 per cent reverse speed to the propeller.

As the name implies, The Twin Disc marine transmission utilizes two disc or plate clutches. This unit also uses helical gears in place of planetary gears for reverse, and since reduction gearing is a built-in feature, forward rotation is also through helical gears.

This is how the Twin Disc transmission works:

Refer to Fig. 122. The principal feature is the duplex clutch. The main clutch castings "A" and "B" are bolted to the engine flywheel and spin with it. In forward, the movable floating plate "C" exerts pressure against the driving plate "D"; for reverse, plate "C" presses against plate "E." These driving plates are attached to their respective shafts by means of splines or teeth which provide the necessary float and assure zero drag in neutral.

When the forward clutch disc is engaged, torque is transmitted directly through a husky drive shaft to the reduction gear pinion. When reverse clutch is clamped, torque is transmitted to a pinion, through reverse idler gear, then to the output gear. The reduction gears are effective in either forward or reverse.

Many modern marine transmissions are referred to as hydraulic. Better nomenclature, perhaps, would be hy-

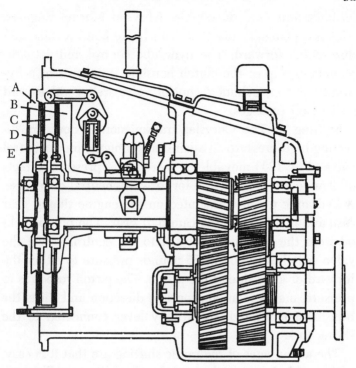

Fig. 122. *Cutaway drawing showing the duplex plate clutch used in the Twin Disc marine transmission. Note the husky helical gears.*

draulically shifted transmission, because power is transmitted in the conventional mechanical way; the shift lever is eliminated and clutch shifting done by internal oil pressure. In hydraulic automobile transmissions, power is actually transmitted through fluid flywheels and hydraulic torque converters; but this is not done in the marine transmission.

Typical of hydraulic marine transmissions is the Chrysler-built unit used on popular Chrysler Marine Engines. This is a planetary machine with brake band reverse and disc clutch forward. The hydraulic control and actuator mounts on top of the clutch housing; it consists of a hydraulic piston, cylinder, control valve, relief valves and various oil passages.

Shifting of The Chrysler transmission is done by directing high pressure oil against a sliding piston. A control valve (Fig. 123) movable by mere finger pressure, directs oil flow to move the piston for forward, neutral or reverse. A hydraulic pump is mounted on the engine timing gear case and is driven by the camshaft gear. The pump sucks oil from the pan and directs it to the control valve; the valve switches the oil at 65 pounds pressure to either the forward or after side of the piston. The piston responds to pressure, moves in an appropriate direction and shifts the transmission through the stubby lever connected to the shifter fork.

The advantages of hydraulic shifting are that it is easy, and can be done swiftly, even by the ladies. It allows remote engine location without long, awkward control linkage. It assures that shifting is done completely, positively, so that clutches are not burned through partial engagement.

General Motors makes a hydraulically operated clutch for their famous marine diesels. This transmission uses two individual plate clutches, one for forward, the other for reverse. An engine-driven pump supplies pressurized oil to a control valve. When the operator flicks the control forward, the valve directs oil to the forward piston plate, an integral part of the forward clutch. High-

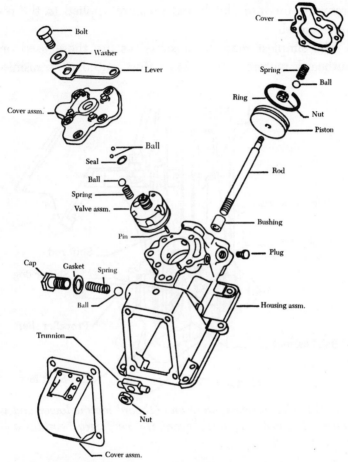

Fig. 123. *The hydraulic control mechanism which mounts on top of the Chrysler marine transmission.*

pressure oil clamps the engine-driven plates to the output plate; rotation is transmitted to the propeller shaft. Naturally, the reverse clutch is maintained neutral. However, when the control is moved to reverse, oil pressure is bled from the forward clutch and pressure applied to the reverse clutch.

The simplest marine transmissions are those used on outboard motors (Fig. 124). Most outboard transmis-

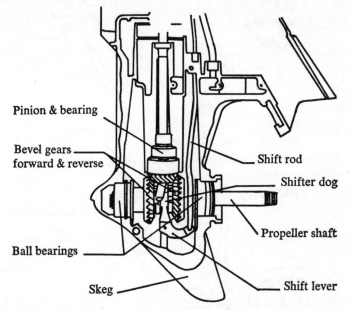

Pinion & bearing

Bevel gears
forward & reverse

Shift rod

Shifter dog

Propeller shaft

Ball bearings

Skeg

Shift lever

Fig. 124. *The transmission in an outboard motors lower unit is simple. It consists of three gears, the necessary bearings and a spline clutch.*

sions consist of but three constant mesh bevel gears, a sliding spline clutch, a shifter fork and three or four bearings. The gears for forward and reverse float on the propeller shaft in constant mesh with the driving gear which is spun by the engine. A slideable dog clutch is splined to the propeller shaft. For clockwise propeller rotation the clutch slides against one gear, locking it to the shaft while the other spins free. For opposite rotation, the clutch frees one gear and locks the other to the shaft. The machine is that simple. Outboard shifts are a little abrupt but are reliable and do a fine job at modest engine speed.

The outboard transmission in the lower unit has the beauty of providing inexpensive, built-in reduction gearing. Reduction gears help the motor swing a good, big propeller and add to overall efficiency.

A few inboard marine transmissions have reduction gears incorporated in the same housing as clutch and reverse gear cluster, but most machines have reduction gears housed in a separate case attached to the business end of the transmission. Of course, most transmissions may be bought without reduction gears; reduction gears cost money; but for most installations they pay their way.

What is the point of reduction gears?

In a nutshell, reduction gears increase propulsive efficiency. This is not just theoretical wind. Most boats driven by high speed engines need reduction gearing between engine and propeller in order to approach top performance and achieve minimum fuel consumption.

It boils down as simple as this: The faster you spin a propeller the more power it wastes on friction. In extreme cases the waste may be a large percentage of absorbed power. Supposing, for example, you made a nicely shaped marine propeller but neglected to give pitch or "bite" to the blades. Then you put the propeller in the water and start to spin it at one thousand r.p.m., two thousand, three, four. Here is your propeller screaming around in the water, delivering absolutely no thrust, but sucking many, many horsepower from the engine just to beat water to froth and fury. This pitchless propeller delivers no useful thrust, yet wastes eight times more power at four thousand r.p.m. than at two thousand.

That leads to this: If a boat is to travel at reasonable speed, the propeller should be correctly proportioned and spun at sensible revolutions. If the engine grinds away at four thousand r.p.m., yet reasonable propeller speed is only two thousand r.p.m., then reduction gears are indicated. A rough rule of thumb is that pitch and diameter should be equal; a "square" propeller usually points to an efficient installation.

Think how silly it would be to push a twelve mile an hour cruiser with four thousand five hundred r.p.m. engine and direct drive transmission. To soak up (and waste) a couple of hundred horsepower we would probably need a twelve-inch diameter propeller, but assuming 50 per cent slip we could only use six-inch pitch. Surely this ridiculous propeller would waste much fuel. How much better to employ 3:1 reduction gears and swing an honest wheel about thirteen inches' diameter and pitch. The boat would go much faster, use less fuel per mile and make less fuss while churning off the knots.

If you doubt the value of reduction gears or question the waste of excess propeller speed, ask yourself why all large aircraft engines mount them: Gears are heavy; weight on aircraft has to be dearly justified.

Lubrication of marine transmissions and reduction gears may be by oil from the engine or by a separate oil system incorporated in the gearbox itself. If the transmission has independent lubrication system, it must be serviced as specified by the manufacturer. Naturally, lack of oil will ruin a transmission pronto.

Some transmissions, especially those with reduction gears, are water cooled by jacketing in the casting. Some have their own separate water system, but most depend upon the engine's cooling system for circulation.

Preventive maintenance on marine transmissions consists mainly of lubrication "by the book" and occasional adjustment of the clutches or reverse bands. Details of adjustment vary widely, but there are some general remarks common to all. If clutch or bands are allowed to wear until slipping starts, heat of friction may destroy the machine. Alternately, if adjustments are made too tight, shifting will be hard or impossible and the transmission may drag badly in neutral. On most hydraulic transmissions it is necessary to adjust the hydraulic-shifting mechanism after clutch and reverse are adjusted. On manually-shifted units it is vitally important that control levers and linkage be husky and stiff so that shifting is firm and positive.

When you install or service clutch linkage, be certain there are no obstructions to prevent full swing of the shift linkage and clutch lever. Be sure that the control hook-up is strong and husky enough to throw the clutch lever home firmly. Flimsy linkage ruins marine transmissions.

Keep spray, rain and bilge water out of the transmission. Nothing will ruin the machine faster than a dose of aqua. If your boat takes on a lot of water and the bilges become a soggy mess, check the transmission; be sure it has not been doused. If you are worried and in doubt, change the oil just for good measure. Remember, most transmissions have a breather opening located low in the bilge. If the breather gets soused, the transmission may be ruined.

Serious misalignment between transmission and propeller shaft is very hard on the machinery and can shorten gearbox life considerably. Misalignment stresses the housing, promotes distortion and throws grinding overloads on the thrust bearing inside the transmission.

At least once a season, break the connection between propeller shaft flange and transmission, then examine the alignment. If necessary, shim the engine until alignment is perfect. Do this when the boat is floating, not when it is hauled, because when hauled the boat may be stressed out of shape. Before aligning engine and shaft, wait until the boat has been afloat a week and has eased back into shape.

Get the habit of slowing the engine before shifting the transmission; it will add to the longevity of the clutches. Jam the lever from forward to reverse, while under power, only in dire emergency. Respect the transmission; give it a little care and it will outlast the engine, the boat and the ship's cat.

Chapter Nineteen

TOOLS AND SPARES ON BOARD

ONE BRIGHT Saturday afternoon last summer we were making a pleasant passage down Vineyard Sound. We had started from the snug little harbor at Cotuit, Cape Cod, and were bound for Cuttyhunk. Our Egg Harbor skiff rolled comfortably with the swells, the breeze was soft from the southwest, the sun warm and things were just right for lazy boating.

Early in the afternoon off of Pasque Island we spotted a boat to the west, apparently in trouble and signaling for help. This seemed strange in such placid weather, but we turned to starboard and approached the troubled boat. It turned out to be a single-screw, 35-foot motorboat with the owner shouting that he had engine trouble. "Will you give me a hand?" he yelled, "I think I've located the trouble."

"Be right over," we shouted, swinging the tool kit over the rail into the dink.

The distressed owner was glad to have a helping hand. "I'm a fair amateur mechanic," he said, "and I am sure that the trouble is that the fuel trap is slugged with water. It has happened before. If I drain it we will be on our way again."

We scratched our head and looked at the trap looming

big as life. "Well why signal for help" we quizzed. "Why not just drain the darned thing?"

He flushed a little and looked like the fox caught in the henhouse: "I forgot my tools."

It was the work of but five minutes with open-end wrench and a tea cup (to keep drippings out of the bilge) and the job was done; the trap was cleared; the engine was restored to usefulness and an embarrassing situation terminated.

There is little need to recall the saying, "For lack of a nail the battle was lost. . . ."

A motorboat is a piece of machinery just like an airplane, automobile or tractor. Machinery requires maintenance, trouble-shooting and tune-up; without tools and spare parts it is impossible to keep a motorboat in shape. Worse, it is impossible to make emergency repairs. A boat is different from car or tractor in one important regard: When away from the shore it is a little world unto itself. The crew cannot walk home. The farther from home a boat operates, the better its tools should be. The farther from shore a boat ventures, the more complete should its spares be. Single-engine power boats should have especially good spares, and tools should be chosen with thought. A well planned tool kit designed for engine maintenance need not be much larger than a doctor's bag and need weigh little more than fifteen pounds.

Here is a kit of tools which will do about any routine job of engine maintenance on the average motor boat:

1. A set of six combination wrenches. These wrenches are open-end type at one end and box wrench on the

other. Six useful sizes are 7/16, 1/2, 9/16, 5/8, 11/16, 3/4; all fractions are in inches, of course (Fig. 125).

2. A socket wrench set having ten sockets from 7/16 to 1 inch. Included in the socket wrench set should be accessories like extensions, reversible ratchet handle and flexible handle. The set should include one special deep socket of correct size to fit the spark plugs on your particular engine. If you want to be a little professional, buy a torque wrench handle for your socket set. The torque wrench is useful when you are installing spark plugs, tightening

Fig. 125. *Combination open end and box wrench. A set of these wrenches is the foundation of a good tool set.*

head nuts or cap screws where torque is critical and specified in the engine manual (Fig. 126).

3. One 6-inch and one 10-inch open-end adjustable wrench. These are the Handy-Andy, all purpose wrenches of the tool kit (Fig. 127).

4. An ignition tool set having midget tools, feeler gauge set, ignition file, small wrenches and a tiny screwdriver. These tools are useful not only for distributor work, but for operations on carburetor, engine instruments and voltage regulator as well (Fig. 131).

5. At least two screwdrivers. One should be stubby for use in tight places. If your machinery has Phillips Head screws, carry one special driver to fit these screws.

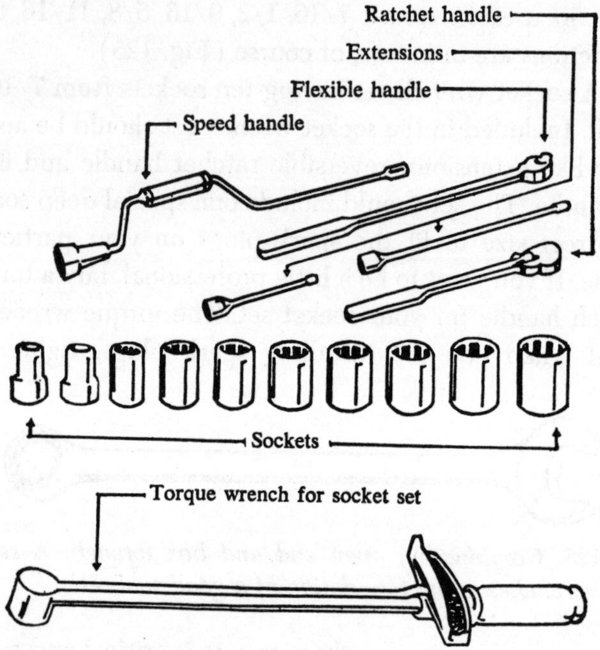

Ratchet handle

Extensions

Flexible handle

Speed handle

Sockets

Torque wrench for socket set

Fig. 126. *A simple but complete socket wrench set for routine marine engine maintenance.*

6. A pair of ordinary slip-joint pliers. No tool box would be complete without a pair of reliable old "gas pipe" pliers. They are handy, but avoid using them in place of correct wrench; they ruin the hex of the nut (Fig. 129).

7. A pair of diagonal cutting pliers. These are useful for all sorts of strange jobs, not only around machinery but even at such jobs as cutting snarled lines from propeller shafts, chewing through broken rigging, cutting fish line and removing snagged fish hooks (Fig. 129).

8. A pair of long nose pliers. These are useful for work

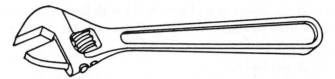

Fig. 127. *An adjustable open end wrench is one of the most versatile tools in the kit.*

with electric wires, handling small parts, reaching into difficult places (Fig. 129).

9. One locking plier wrench. These are sometimes called vise grips and can be used in a hundred ways. They

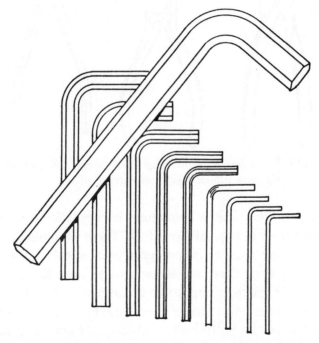

Fig. 128. *A set of Allen wrenches for socket set screws.*

have terrific leverage and bite down with fierce grip. They can be used as pliers, wrench or vise. A most useful tool (Fig. 130).

10. A penknife.

11. A light ball peen hammer.

12. An Allen set screw wrench set. These little

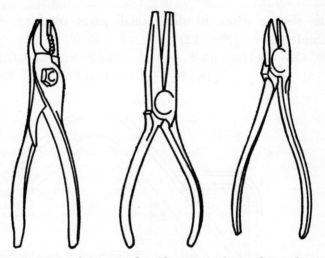

Fig. 129. *From left to right: Slip joint pliers, the jack of all trades; Long nose pliers; Diagonal cutting pliers.*

wrenches look like a miniature hockey stick and are formed from hexagonal steel stock. There is nothing more exasperating than to encounter a gear or collar fixed in place by a recessed set screw and to lack the proper wrench. It is almost impossible to improvise (Fig. 128).

The twelve items form a good basic tool set for routine maintenance on motorboat machinery. At current prices, this set should cost about $50.00, of which $20.00 would

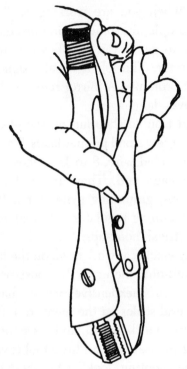

Fig. 130. *Locking plier wrench, or vise grip pliers. This tool has a compound lever action which makes it bite with fierce pressure.*

go into the socket wrench set. Half a C note is a respectable amount of money, but not much compared to a real panic situation aboard your boat brought on by sick machinery and lack of tools.

There are some items, in addition to basic tools, which come in handy and ease the harried mechanic's life: A flashlight is most useful around machinery buried deep in the bilge. A mirror, like those ladies carry in their purse, is a fine tool when you are working on "upside down" places. For example, on some engine installations it is all but impossible to get at the float bowl drain plug on the updraft carburetor. The job is usually done by feel and with the aid of profanity. A mirror reduces skinned knuckles and improves language.

Tune-up and trouble shooting on the electrical system are speeded by a few small jumper leads. These are lengths of insulated, stranded wire, 8 to 12 inches long, with alligator clips on each end. They are useful for jumping doubtful switches, grounding generator field terminal to test for malfunctioning regulator, and making all kinds of temporary electrical hook-ups.

If you do any electrical work at all on the boat's machinery, a small volt-ohm-meter is the most useful piece of gear possible. An inexpensive v.o.m. has a selector switch and several scales on the meter to indicate voltage from a few volts to a thousand, and resistance from a few ohms to tens of thousands. This little tool is valuable when you are trouble shooting, looking for short circuits, open circuits, excess voltage loss through wires, poor connections, blown fuses or malfunctioning components.

Next best to a v.o.m. is a trouble shooting light. This is a 6 volt or 12 volt light bulb and socket with 12-inch leads and test prods. It may be used to find dead circuits, open switches, blown fuses and so on.

A hydrometer is useful not only for testing the condition of storage batteries, but also for adding water to the cells. But if you carry a battery hydrometer aboard, do not store it with the other tools lest drops of acid eat into the wrenches and pliers.

Spare parts are like a first-aid kit. You carry good materials but hope they will be unnecessary. The quantity of spares depends upon how far you go from shore, the kind of water you cruise and how much risk you care to take.

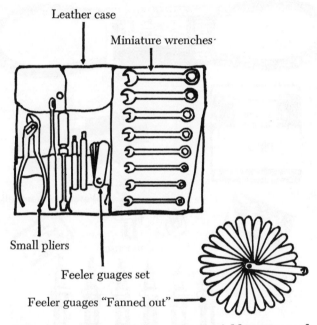

Fig. 131. *An ignition tool set consists of liliputian tools designed for adjusting small, delicate parts.*

For equal safety, an auxiliary or motor sailer requires fewer spare parts than a straight power boat. Twin-engine boats require less than single.

Common sense dictates that spare parts should be carried for parts or assemblies which are likely to fail at sea and which can be replaced at sea with ordinary tools.

Here is a suggested list of spare parts for a gasoline-powered boat which cruises outside the home harbor (Fig. 132):

1. A spare spark plug or complete set of plugs.

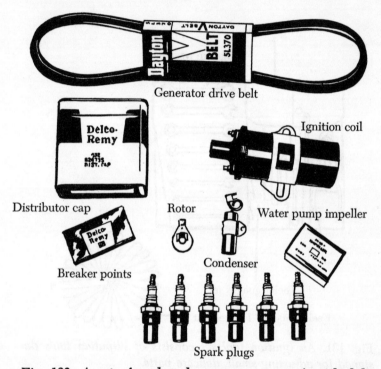

Generator drive belt

Ignition coil

Distributor cap

Rotor

Water pump impeller

Breaker points

Condenser

Spark plugs

Fig. 132. *A set of on-board emergency parts furnished by Palmer Engine Co., for one of their marine engines.*

2. A set of ignition breaker points and a condenser. The point and condenser set is probably the most important set of spares aboard because the parts are delicate and vulnerable. Without them the engine is dead.

3. A distributor cap. A spare cap is an important spare because the part is fragile, and a cracked cap can stop the engine.

4. A distributor rotor. This part is fragile, like the cap, and if it breaks, the ignition system is out of commission.

5. An ignition coil. A spare coil should be carried because it is all but impossible to repair a dud at sea, or in the shop, for that matter.

6. A fuel pump. A spare pump is desirable because pumps generally fail without warning. Under extreme conditions it is possible to improvise some kind of jury rig fuel system on which to limp home, but it is both difficult and dangerous. An alternative is to carry a fuel pump rebuild kit.

7. A carburetor. This is an outright extravagance but we carry one on our boat. Carburetors seem to function beautifully until the weather becomes foul and the sea kicks up. Then they get slugged with dirt. It is quicker to bolt on a new one than to fool with the sick one under rotten conditions.

8. Proper type and sizes of fuse. (Spare light bulbs are handy, too.)

9. A watertight jar full of assorted cotters, nuts, bolts, clevis pins, washers, clips, screws, packing, elastic bands. A jar of "junk" is invaluable when you are puttering or making emergency repairs at sea.

10. A box of miscellaneous stuff including such things as a can of penetrating oil, spools of wire, gasket compound, electrical tape, small grease gun, nylon cord, copper tubing, fuel line fittings.

If you are handy around electrical and electronic gear, a junk box of assorted resistors, capacitors, switches, relays, terminal blocks and similar stuff will be handy.

Tools and spare parts aboard your boat will decay into a mound of rust and corrosion unless cared for. Keep the spares wrapped in waxed paper or polyethylene bags and store them aboard in the driest place possible. Tools must be handy to be useful; they cannot be wrapped up and hidden, but they can be oiled and protected. If a tool gets wet, dry and oil it as soon as possible. When you go ashore for any period, take tools home and keep them dry.

Adequate spare parts and good tools can contribute a lot to happy cruising. Granted, a breakdown may not endanger the boat or cause risk to the crew, but may, nevertheless, cause acute embarrassment and ruin what would have otherwise been a nice passage. A few minutes spent on checking tools and spares may contribute lots toward pleasurable cruising, and the few dollars spent may come back with interest.

INDEX

HART

PUBLISHING

COMPANY